the Forth
Naturalist
and Historian

Volume 12

Forth Naturalist and Historian, volume 12

Published by the Forth Naturalist and Historian Editorial Board,
The University, Stirling, 1990

The Board is a University/Central Regional Council collaboration.

ISSN 0309-7560

ISBN 0 9514147 3 9

Single copies may be taken of single articles in this journal provided due
acknowledgement is made and the copies are for non-profit education or private
use.

Supported by BP in Scotland.

Cover – based on the 1566 Seton Armorial, by courtesy of the Trustees
of the National Library of Scotland.

Printed by Meigle Printers Ltd., Tweedbank Industrial Estate, Galashiels.
Set in Palacio on Sequel Matt Art Paper.

ANNUAL CLIMATOLOGICAL BULLETIN NO. 10, 1988

S. J. Harrison
University of Stirling

THE WEATHER OF 1988

Temperature and rainfall values referred to in the following relate to Stirling Parkhead unless otherwise stated.

In climatological terms 1988 was not a particularly exceptional year, but mean temperature was surprisingly 0.6°C above average, and most remarkable was the sudden shift in weather conditions from June to July between which maximum temperatures changed from 2.2°C above normal to 2.5°C below, and rainfall from 28% to 311% of normal. July was the wettest in Scotland since 1869. December was one of the mildest on record and was frost-free in many places. Some December days were actually warmer than in July!! On the more spectacular side, ball-lightning, a very rare occurrence in central Scotland, was observed during September. Elsewhere the most newsworthy items included the long-term impact of the Greenhouse Effect and the now famous Ozone Hole, the drought in North America, and the hurricanes which afflicted the coasts of the Caribbean and the Gulf of Mexico.

January. Mild, damp and rather windy

As a complex and deep area of low pressure and its associated fronts moved eastwards across Scotland over the first three days, winds were fresh to strong WSW. Local rainfall was moderate in contrast to southern England and South Wales which experienced stormy conditions and flooding. As the low became stationary and filled on the 4th and 5th winds became light and night temperatures fell below freezing. Freezing fog late on the 4th was replaced by an overnight fall of snow which turned to rain on the 5th. With winds coming from the north, the 6th and 7th were cold days, but Atlantic systems returned mild wet weather on the 8th which persisted until the 15th. As skies cleared briefly on the 11th, night temperatures fell, resulting in severe black ice. High pressure extended briefly from the south-west on the 15th and winds became light. Minimum temperatures fell early on the 18th as the sky cleared behind a cold front (−2.7°C, −5.1°C at Carim). A vigorous depression which tracked north-eastwards across Scotland over the 18th and 19th brought heavy rain and snow in a strong south-easterly which resulted in some local flooding and gale damage. As pressure increased behind the system, temperatures fell in a cold arctic airstream and snow affected some

Scottish roads. Snow was more widespread on the 23rd and league football was badly affected throughout Britain. The weather remained unsettled and cold for the rest of the month with pressure remaining low. The last day of the month saw the Meteorological Office issuing severe weather warnings as a deep depression approached from the west.

February. Continuing mild and wet.

The weather was very unsettled over the first three days with heavy rain in a fresh to strong south-westerly wind. As an area of low pressure became slow moving over the northern North Sea on the 4th the wind dropped but snow fell in many parts of Scotland, blocking the A9 on the 6th. The wind began to strengthen again on the 8th as another deep depression crossed northern Scotland. The 9th was stormy with heavy snow on high ground and pressure fell to 948mb in the afternoon (compare this with the October 1987 'hurricane' in southern England when pressure fell to only 958mb!) By the end of the 10th the system had moved towards Norway and the wind slackened. A cold arctic airstream kept temperatures low until the 12th and some snow fell on higher ground. Vigorous fronts brought in milder air with rain on the 13th as they lingered over southern Scotland the weather remained dull and wet. High pressure built over the UK from the 16th but although the wind became light the weather remained unsettled with some lengthy sunny periods. As the anticyclone drifted westwards, a strong northerly airstream developed on the 28th in which visibility was excellent.

March. Cold at first becoming mild and wet.

While pressure remained high to the west of the British Isles the wind remained in the north or north-west. Light sleet fell on the 5th, otherwise the first few days of the month were cold and dry. After the 9th the anticyclone began to drift southwards and the wind moved around to a more westerly quarter. Night temperature fell sharply as a ridge extended southwards over Scotland on the 13th, reaching −5.5°C by 09.00 on the 14th. Heavy rain on the 15th was preceded by snow. Daytime temperatures stayed below freezing all day on the 14th at the Ochil Hills station. The weather was changeable as a series of frontal troughs separated by weak ridges moved rapidly eastwards across Scotland until the 23rd. A deep low became slow moving to the north of Scotland after the 24th which was a windy and very wet day. Further frontal troughs after the 27th brought a period of dull wet weather which cleared on the 31st as pressure increased from the south-west.

April. Mild but a very wet month.

Continuous rain fell on the 1st as weak fronts moved south-eastwards across Scotland, but by the 2nd pressure began to increase from both east and west. By the 3rd high pressure was centred over northern Britain and the weather became calm, sunny and warm until the 7th, when a cold front began to move slowly southwards into Scotland. The maximum temperature reached 17.8°C on the 6th, which was hot and sunny. In contrast, Easter Monday morning (4th) was foggy (20m or less) before the sun broke through. As a cold front crossed Scotland on the 8th snow showers fell in the evening. There was one more day of bright sunshine on the 9th before more active weather systems with rain began to replace the anticyclone. Small amounts of rain fell each day until a ridge cleared the sky overnight on the 12th giving a sharp early morning frost (−3.8°C) Bridge of Allan; −4.8°C Carim). Rain returned late on the 14th heralding a period of dull wet weather up to the 21st. A depression became slow moving to the west of Ireland by the 16th and its associated fronts affected Scotland on the 18th bringing the wettest day of the month (26.4mm). A ridge of high pressure extended southwards across Scotland on the 22nd to cover all of Britain by the 25th. The wind, however, remained generally easterly and the weather cloudy and dull. When the skies cleared the weather became sunny and warm, reaching 19.3°C on the 24th. A shallow low developed in a col on the 25th bringing light rain. The clouds cleared briefly again on the 28th giving a bright clear opening day for the Glasgow Garden Festival after the last of the spring air frosts in the lowlands (−0.6°C at Bridge of Allan). A deep depression was approaching from the south-west on the 30th.

May. Warm with occasional rain.

As a deep low became slow moving to the south-west of Ireland continuous moderate rain fell on the 1st in a fresh easterly wind (16.7mm). The weather remained cyclonic dull and damp but as pressure began to rise on the 5th the sky cleared a little to give two sunny and very warm days on the 6th and 7th. Although the 8th saw a brief return to dull weather, the 9th and 10th were again sunny. The weather between the 11th and 13th was cyclonic but on the 14th a ridge extended southwards. The 15th was the warmest day of the month (19.6°C). As high pressure drifted to a position south of Iceland on the 17th, a northerly breeze caused temperatures to fall sharply behind a southwards moving cold front which was followed by light showers, some of which fell as snow on high ground. The last spring frost at Carim occurred on the 18th (−2.6°C). The high drifted eastwards across Britain between the 20th and 22nd which were bright and sunny. A vigorous low and associated fronts came in its wake and the 23rd and 24th were dull and very wet (21.4mm). The low became slow moving, filled to the north-west and was followed by another low which tracked northwards through Ireland between the 28th and 31st. Rain during the afternoon of the 29th was torrential and was accompanied by thunder and lightning.

June. Very warm and exceptionally dry.

A slow moving depression moved eastwards across Scotland between the 1st and the 4th. Showery rain fell on all four days but amounts were very small (5.5mm total). Pressure rose steadily between the 5th and 8th from 1017mb to 1026mb where it stayed almost without change until the last three days of the month. The weather was not always sunny and warm, many days starting dull but clearing later. Weak frontal troughs crossed Scotland on several occasions but in the main produced little more than periods of dull oppressive weather with light drizzle amounting to very little measureable rainfall (eg 0.2mm on the 14th). Slightly more vigorous troughs moved south-eastwards on the 20th and 21st but again rainfall amounts were minute. Daytime temperatures exceeded 20°C on 13 days, reaching 24.4°C on the 13th and 14th when temperatures exceeded 21°C at Carim. As the high pressure retreated south-westwards, pressure began to fall over Scotland on the 25th and rain fell overnight on the 25th/26th in a cool westerly breeze (7.8mm). An extensive area of low pressure, which had been pushing westwards from continental Europe, brought more cloudy dull weather by the 27th but on most day clouds had cleared away by late morning. There were very heavy showers with local thunder on the 30th.

July. Very unsettled, cool and very wet.

The change from the warmth and dryness of June was dramatic and immediate. A complex low with associated frontal troughs moved into Scotland on the 1st bringing fresh winds and heavy thundery showers. The 24-hour fall of 25.5mm at Parkhead made it the wettest day of the month. As the depression deepened on the 2nd and 3rd winds increased bringing driving rain to much of Britain. The low filled very rapidly and between the 4th and 8th drifted slowly northwards to Shetland. There was occasional rain with some longer spells of clearer sunny weather, although the 6th was again a very wet day (12.7mm). By the 9th, Atlantic systems began to bring yet more rain but in a fresher westerly airstream. A weak ridge developed over Britain on the 14th and 15th which dried up the weather a little but further frontal troughs moved in to bring rain again on the 16th. Another weak ridge on the 19th gave not only a dry day but the month's warmest, reaching a lowly 19.8°C! The ridge gave way to a complex cyclonic pattern late on the 20th heralding the return of a wet spell which lasted to the end of the month. The 22nd to 24th was particularly wet, accumulating 42.9mm at Parkhead (40.2mm in

Bridge of Allan). A deep low crossed to the north of Scotland on the 25th resulting in some localised gale damage and Glasgow Airport experienced its strongest winds in July for at least 50 years. In the strong WSW wind showers were frequent and occasionally heavy on the 26th and 27th. The weather remained unsettled and wet for the remainder of the month, bringing to an end the wettest July in Scotland since 1869.

August. Warm at first, becoming cool and wet.

Pressure remained high to the south-west of Britain for the first five days but frontal troughs crossing Scotland kept the weather unsettled. Heavy thundery showers fell on the 1st. an anticyclone moved north-eastwards across Britain between the 5th and 7th which were warm and generally dry days. In its wake came a complex low in which the weather was exceptionally warm but very humid. Daytime temperatures exceeded 24°C on the 7th, 8th, and 9th, rain falling as a weak frontal trough moved eastwards late on the 8th. The weather remained unsettled until the 14th and a deep depression cross north-west Scotland on the 13th and 14th when there was exceptionally heavy overnight rain (23.5mm). Atlantic fronts returned late on the 17th dumping a further 49.0mm of rain on Stirling over three days. The 21st and 22nd were dry and pleasantly sunny as pressure rose, but for the remainder of the month frontal troughs kept the weather unsettled. A deep depression became slow moving to the north of Scotland by the 27th and the last few days were windy and wet. The import of cold arctic air into the rear of the depression kept daytime temperatures well below the seasonal average. The month's rainfall was 189% of the average.

September. Generally unsettled but dry mid-month.

The 1st saw a deep depression centred over Northern Ireland, which made for a windy and wet start to the month. The 13.7mm of rain was the highest 24-hour total of the month. Behind the depression, showers fell in a cool westerly breeze until the 5th when pressure began to build from the east. The very warm southerly airstream brought in warm humid weather culminating in heavy thundery rain overnight on the 7th. During the storms property in Dunblane and Dunning was damaged by ball lightning (See Note 4). Another area of high pressure, to the west of Ireland by the 11th, moved only a short distance eastwards over the following six days. Days were cool, sunny and dry in a light north-westerly breeze. As the high began to move southwards from the 18th the wind backed westerly and cloud amounts increased. The 20th and 21st were cool with cloud shrouding the local hills. Depressions and a succession of frontal troughs brought a return to unsettled weather after the 21st, the 22nd being particularly wet (13.4mm). The wind was at times strong to gale force. Cold arctic air in the wake of a depression on the 28th gave the first light falls of snow on the Scottish hills. As pressure rose the sky cleared, resulting in the first air-frosts of the autumn early on the 30th.

October. Mild and wet.

A very deep depression brushed north-west Scotland on the 1st and rain fell from its trailing cold front in the afternoon. The front lingered over Scotland for a couple of dull damp days before vigorous depressions moved in from the north-west. The 4th to the 8th were wet with 43.8mm of rain. The sky cleared under a ridge of high pressure on the 10th and frosts were registered in Bridge of Allan on the 10th and 11th ($-0.3°C$, $-0.7°C$). In contrast, a depression over South-West England at the same time gave 50mm of rain and severe local flooding. By the 14th a more substantial area of high pressure had extended south-westwards across Britain from Scandinavia. Although remaining dry up to the 17th, the weather was foggy, the worst day being the 15th when dense fog cleared for only two hours during the afternoon. Air temperatures rose quickly on the 17th as the high retreated eastwards bringing Britain into a very mild southerly airstream. Low pressure and a large number of associated troughs ensured that the 18th to 27th were mostly dull and wet. Rain late on the 25th was very heavy (21.2mm) and the Allan reached the top of its banks. As high pressure returned to Scotland the sky cleared and night temperatures fell below freezing on the remaining days, dropping to $-3.2°C$ and heralding a change to colder winter weather.

November. Cold at times and dry.

An anticyclone moved from south-east of Iceland to cross the British Isles over the first four days. Cloud amounts were generally small which resulted in night temperatures falling below freezing. A weak frontal trough moved south-eastwards across Scotland late on the 4th but rainfall was only slight. The 5th and 6th were again cool and sunny but evenings were misty. As high pressure retreated into continental Europe Scotland was brought into a dull and cloudy but very mild southerly airstream. Light drizzle fell on the 7th and on the morning of the 8th visibility was down to less than 50m. A depression and associated fronts tracked north-eastwards on the 8th and 9th bringing continuous moderate rain (48hr total 22.0mm) but low clouds cleared and visibility improved as a cold front crossed Scotland on the 10th. With low pressure to the north and high pressure to the south, a fresh to strong south-westerly breeze brought two fresh days on the 11th and 12th with brief rainy spells. High pressure returned by the 13th but, although the 14th was bright and sunny, anticyclonic gloom persisted until the 16th keeping night temperatures above freezing. A depression tracked rapidly eastwards on the 17th but as pressure began to increase in its wake a cold and raw northerly wind began to blow. As a shallow low crossed Scotland on the 19th the first snow of the winter fell on low ground but to a depth of only 2cm. High pressure moved in from the west on the 20th and, while it lingered in the vicinity of the British Isles, days were cool with moderate night frosts until the 27th. The daytime temperature stayed below freezing at Carim ($-1.4°C$) on the 20th. More unsettled weather moved in from the Atlantic late on the 27th and temperatures rose very quickly in the milder air. Frontal troughs brought rain which was heavy and continuous on the 29th (18.5mm), the wettest day of the month.

December. Exceptionally mild.

While an anticyclone lingered over the eastern Baltic, the wind over Britain was a cold and raw easterly. The maximum temperature reached only 4.2°C on the 22nd (1.2°C at Carim). A deep depression moved across Scotland on the 3rd and 4th which were wet and windy, but considerably milder. Pressure rose very quickly on the 5th and 6th, which cleared away the cloud and caused night temperatures to dip a little below freezing. Although pressure remained high, a series of weak troughs brought cloud and occasional slight rain until the 16th. Both maximum and minimum temperatures were as much as 5°C higher than the seasonal average. By the end of the 17th frontal troughs were moving in from the west and the wind was freshening westerly as high pressure retreated southwards. For the next ten days the weather was unsettled with periods of rain, which was heavy at times. Deep depressions crossed to the north of Scotland between the 21st and 23rd which were blustery wet days. Rainfall amounts were, however, moderately small. The sky cleared briefly under a ridge of high pressure late on the 23rd, which resulted in only the second air-frost of the month ($-0.3°C$). Frontal troughs restored less settled weather by 22.00 on Christmas Day and by 09.00 the next day 12.3mm of rain had fallen. The next two days remained dull and wet but by the 28th, pressure had begun to build again from the east. Air temperatures in a very mild south-westerly airstream were remarkably high, the maximum temperature reaching 14.0°C on the 28th, 6.9°C higher than the seasonal average. The minimum recorded in Bridge of Allan exceeded 10°C on the 29th (8.0°C at Carim). For many places this was the mildest December on record and the talk was of the 'Greenhouse Effect' (See Note 3).

DATA SOURCES

Stirling (Parkhead)
Grid Reference: NS 815 969 – University gardens. Height above sea-level: 35m.   Aspect: South-east.   Shelter Index: 33.2 (Slightly sheltered).   Established 1970.   Monthly returns of daily observations are submitted to the Meteorological Office and the Climatological Observers Link. Missing air temperature data have been estimated by cross reference to data from Bridge of Allan station. Since 1987 weekly observations have been made of ground-level rainfall and run-of-wind. Some of the conventional data have been of dubious quality and have been corrected by cross-referencing.

Ochil Hills (Carim)
Grid Reference: NN 864 049 — upper catchment of the Burn of Ogilvie near to the ruined Carim Lodge. Surrounded by open moorland. Height above sea-level: 332m.   Aspect: North-west.   Shelter Index: 16.6 (Exposed).   Established: 1980.   An autographic recording station serviced on Mondays. Very few days of data were lost during 1988. The raingauge was unreliable and did not provide an adequate basis for the determination of daily totals. Monthly totals have been derived from the weekly figures. Sub-division of weekly totals overlapping between months has been calculated on a proportional basis using Stirling (Parkhead). The Automatic Weather Station was out of action throughout 1988 due entirely to the manufacturer's inability to provide equipment which worked!

Bridge of Allan
Grid Reference: NS 795 964 — A suburban back-garden station. Mature Norway Spruce trees to the west, houses and garages from north-west to north-east, otherwise open aspect across the Carse of Stirling (Forth Valley).   Height above sea-level: 10m.   Established: 1984. Non-standard equipment and exposure. Six's Max-Min thermometer on a north facing post at 1.8m above ground level; calibrated regularly. Home-made plastic rain gauge conforming as far as possible to standard.

CLIMATOLOGICAL AVERAGES

Climatological averages are usually calculated for periods of 30 years (temperature) or 35 years (rainfall), since in Britain there is an inbuilt year to year variation in all the parameters used to define climate. Averages based on a smaller number of years may be unduly biased by one extreme value. As there are only 18 years of records for Stirling (Parkhead) and 8 for Ochil Hills (Carim) the averages published in Tables 7 and 8 should be used with caution.

NOTES

1 1988. A Summer of Contrasts

One of the exceptional featurs of 1988 was the very rapid change in the weather from June to July, from hot and dry to cold and very wet. Figure 1(a) indicates that in June most of Britain was drier than usual but that this was most marked in Scotland. Although mean minimum temperatures were generally well above average, south-east of a line from the Wash to the Severn Estuary they were well below. Mean maximum temperatures were generally as much as 2°C or more higher than average. In July, the whole of the British Isles was generally cold and wet, although in Scotland there was a tendency for the west to receive the worst of the weather (Figure 1(b)). Stornoway, for example, received 229% of its average while Dyce had only 111% (Royal Meteorological Society Weather Log).

2 Hurricane Gilbert

During 1988 attention was turned to weather events overseas and in particular Hurricane Gilbert which wreaked havoc through the Caribbean and the Gulf of Mexico between the 9th and 17th of September. The US National Hurricane Centre in Miami described the storm as the most intense on record. Jamaica, which lay directly in its path (Figure 2), was devastated. 500,000 were made homeless and the University of the West Indies was severely damaged. The next landfalls, the Yucatan Peninsula and Mexico, were also hit very badly. The Saffir/Simpson scale of hurricane damage potential has five points, category five having sustained winds over 157mph and pressure in the eye less than 920mb. Hurricane Gilbert was in this 'catastrophic' category for 31 hours, reaching a remarkable centre pressure of 885mb during the evening of the 13th, not long after it had passed over Jamaica. Maximum sustained wind speeds exceeded 175mph and gusts topped 200mph. It makes the October 1987 so-called 'hurricane' in south-east England look like a fresh breeze! The above notes have been extracted from an excellent report — Eden, P. 1988 Hurricane Gilbert *Weather* 43, 446-448.

3 A Warm Year. The Greenhouse Effect??

With maximum temperatures exceeding the long-term average during 10 months out of 12 and plants and wildlife switching into spring activity by the end of December, there has been considerable speculation that this could be in some way linked to a general global warming resulting from an enhanced greenhouse effect. This effect is due to the absorptive properties of gases and aerosols in the lower atmosphere which absorb very little of incoming solar radiation but which absorb most of the long-wave infra-red radiation emitted by the Earth's surface. The principal gases involved are carbon dioxide and water vapour which together provide the vital thermal blanket which protects the surface from excessive heat loss to space, such as occurs on the Moon. The problems have arisen because of steady increases in the carbon dioxide content resulting principally from the combustion of fossil fuels, in gases such as methane, and in aerosols such as CFC's.

The likely outcome would appear to be a general increase in the temperature of the troposphere but to leave this as an unqualified statement would be unduly simplistic and misleading. The complex interrelationships which exist in atmospheric processes means that we must also consider the changes in the atmospheric circulation and water balance resulting from any possible warming. Most predictions of the likely outcome of the enhanced greenhouse effect indicate very complex patterns of change with some areas experiencing more or less precipitation, in addition to which weather patterns may oscillate more markedly between extremes. It is true that air temperatures have generally increased since the mid-19thC alongside measured carbon dioxide content in the lower atmosphere, but we must ask ourselves whether such an apparent correlation is based on a real cause-effect relationship. What is known is that the Earth began to recover from a period referred to as the 'Little Ice Age' after the mid-19thC. The observed changes in temperature can, to some extent, be attributed to a natural process of recovery from this colder period.

As to the current year with its continued upward trend in annual rainfall, apparent increase in weather extremes and general mildness, it is tempting to lay the blame at the door of the greenhouse effect, but we can not reach such conclusions with any degree of confidence and at this stage we must not dismiss the possibility of mundane 'natural fluctuation'. It is interesting to note that the so-called scientific writers who now point us towards the 'certain' effects of global warming were equally certain during the 1970s about the coming Ice Age!!

4 Ball Lightning

In September there were observations of what appears to have been ball lightning in Dunblane and Dunning. Fortunately this is a rare phenomenon here in central Scotland. It occurs immediately after a lightning strike, which can contain as much as 1GJ of energy, and lasts no longer than a few minutes. Ninety percent of the balls are spherical and have a median diameter of 25cm. They are a result of the ionisation of the atmosphere which is converted into a plasma in which each atom or molecule in the air loses one electron. The energy stored in the plasma (1MJ) remains there until released, sometimes through contact with a solid object, when it is converted into light, heat and sound. A little over half of ball lightning dissipates with a loud explosion.

See: Lewis, H. W. 1980. Ball Lightning, in Lynch, D. K. (Editor) *Atmospheric Phenomena*. Freeman.

Stenoff, M. 1985. Ball Lightning. *Journal of Meteorology* 10 (100), 231-235.

5 Effects of Elevation   Figures 3, 4 and 5

During 1988 the average difference in daily maximum air temperature between Stirling (Parkhead) and Ochil Hills (Carim) stations was 4.1°C which is equivalent to a lapse-rate of 13.8°C per 1000m which is exceptionally steep and well in excess of the long-term average of 10.8°C per 1000m. The average difference in minimum temperatures was 1.4°C, or a lapse rate of 4.7°C per 1000m, again greater than the average (4.0). The difference in mean temperature was 2.7°C, representing a lapse-rate of 9.1°C per 1000m. These exceptionally steep lapse-rates are consistent with the high frequency of unstable atmospheric conditions during 1988. This is in marked contrast to 1987 when the elevation effect was subdued by a high frequency of stable and dry atmospheric conditions. This last year, studies have been undertaken into the thermal growing season in the Ochil Hills and into the difference in freeze-thaw frequencies. The growing season is delayed at the Ochil Hills station by up to five or six weeks. Freeze-thaw frequency is based on the number of days during which maximum temperatures remain above freezing and minimum temperatures drop below. During the autumn and early winter months there is a greater frequency of freeze-thaw days in Stirling than there is at Carim. Later in the winter and in spring the difference is reversed. The differences in annual precipitation between the two stations during 1988 was 604.3mm giving a gradient of change of 2.03mm/m. This compares with the 1981-88 average of 1.73mm/m.

6 Rainfall Trends   Figure 6

The low annual rainfall total in 1987 appears to have been a minor setback in the long-term trend. The total for 1988, 1106.6mm, tends to confirm an upward trend, but examination of the highest 24 hour falls shows that large falls in excess of 30mm have been absent again. There was no major overtopping of the banks of the River Allan during 1988, nor has there been since Philippa Rowling completed her award-winning dissertation on Bridge of Allan floods up to 1986. It is, perhaps, ironic that only now has a flood protection scheme been commenced.

Rowling, P. 1989. Rainfall variation and some implications for flooding in the Allan catchment, central Scotland *Weather*. 44(4), 146-154.

7 Climatic Hazards Unit — 1988 Activities

Professor Smith was awarded a contract with British Rail to study the effect of the weather on train operations. Mr D. Mukherjee, a postgraduate student of Civil Engineering from Birmingham University, has been appointed as post-doctoral research assistant on this project. Jackie Vale, Dr Harrison's research student on the Severn Estuary Aerial Inputs programme, has now completed her first year and has established a new pollution monitoring network. The Meteorological Office funded two meetings organised by the Unit. The first, in February, was on 'Weather Sensitivity and Services in Scotland' and examined the perception of weather impact on various aspects of the Scottish economy and the services provided by the Meteorological Office. The proceedings are to be published by Scottish Academic Press. The second was a workshop on 'Weather Information for Tourism and Outdoor Recreation' which explored how inputs of weather information can be of value in the further development of the Scottish tourist industry. A report of this meeting has been produced.

8 Schools Contacts

Dr Harrison helped to organise a one-day workshop in October 1988 for teachers of physical geography one aspect of which was 'weather study'. Notes were produced on project design and data sources, which are available for £2 from S. J. Harrison, Environmental Science, University of Stirling. Further in-service training courses are planned for March/April 1989 (independent schools) and September/October (Strathclyde schools). Assistance given to Highers Geography pupils has increased dramatically during 1988 and to date well over 20 have been helped in some way. At present there are no plans to introduce charges for this service. Environmental Science may also hold an Information Day for teachers during 1989 and there is a University Open Day on Friday September 15th. Dr Harrison has recently been appointed an Associate Schools Liaison Officer by the University.

9 Register of Weather Stations

A second supplement to the Register of Weather Stations has been produced. This contains details of recent additions to the Register plus corrections. Copies are available for £1.05 from the Climatic Hazards Unit. We regret that all copies of the original Register have now been sold. If there is sufficient demand it may be possible to produce a second edition during 1990. Comments would be welcome.

10 Reference Material

The Microclimatology Laboratory and the Climatic Hazards Room contain an increasing amount of reference material including climatic data (local, national, and global), synoptic weather data and scientific reports.

Use of these data in publications should be acknowledged.

11 Publications during 1988 by Environmental Science Department.

Harrison, S. J. Climatic conditions over the Estuary and Firth of Forth. *Proceedings of the Royal Society of Edinburgh* 93B, 245-258.
Harrison, S. J. Numerical assessment of local shelter around weather stations. *Weather* 43, 325-330.
Harrison, S. J. and Harrison, D. J. The effect of elevation on the climatically determined growing season in the Ochil Hills. *Scottish Geographical Magazine* 104, 108-115.
Harrison, S. J. and Harrison D. J. The effect of altitude on freeze-thaw frequency. *Journal of Meteorology* 13 (113), 341-343.
Harrison, S. J. *Register of Weather Station Supplement No. 2*. Climatic Hazards Unit.
Smith, K. Avalanche hazards: the rising death toll. *Geography* 73, 157-158.
Smith, K. Highway meteolorology comes to Scotland. *Scottish Geographical Magazine* 104, 60-62.
Smith, K. Future trends in atmospheric data and services. *Weather* 43, 401-405.

Single copies of the Annual Climatological Bulletin are available to schools free of charge. Further copies cost £1 each and are obtainable from the Department of Environmental Science, Stirling University.

	Mean Maximum °C	Difference from Average	Highest Maximum	Lowest Maximum	Mean Minimum °C	Difference from Average	Highest Minimum	Lowest Minimum	Mean °C	No. days No. of <0°C	Mean Soil Temp. °C (0.3m at 09)
January	6·7	+0·9	11·5	3·0	1·6	+1·6	6·0	−2·8	4·1	4	3·8
February	7·4	+1·2	12·0	4·2	1·4	+1·0	5·8	−2·4	4·4	6	3·3
March	8·9	+0·4	13·8	4·0	1·2	−0·3	7·6	−8·2	5·0	9	4·6
April	12·3	+0·7	19·3	5·0	4·3	+1·2	8·3	0·0	8·3	0	8·3
May	15·7	+0·8	19·6	11·4	5·7	+0·2	9·3	1·1	10·7	0	11·6
June	19·6	+2·2	25·8	15·3	10·2	+1·9	13·2	6·2	14·9	0	16·0
July	17·1	−2·5	19·8	13·4	9·9	−0·8	15·4	5·9	13·5	0	15·9
August	18·7	−0·4	26·4	14·7	9·8	−0·1	14·8	5·2	14·2	0	16·3
September	16·5	+0·6	21·9	12·2	8·2	0·0	14·2	−0·8	12·3	0	14·5
October	13·7	+1·1	18·0	10·3	6·0	+0·5	10·8	−3·2	9·8	1	11·0
November	9·4	+0·6	12·4	5·3	0·7	−1·7	6·7	−4·0	5·0	13	6·8
December	10·3	+3·2	14·0	4·2	3·4	+1·9	6·5	−0·3	6·8	2	5·7
YEAR	13·0	+0·7	26·4	3·0	5·2	+0·4	15·4	−8·2	9·1	35	9·8

Table 1   Monthly Temperatures (Stirling, Parkhead) 1988

* = Some Missing Values	Mean Maximum °C	Difference from Average	Highest Maximum	Lowest Maximum	Mean Minimum °C	Difference from Average	Highest Minimum	Lowest Minimum	Mean °C	Difference Parkhead to Carim	No. days < 0°C
January	2·9	+0·5	10·8	− 0·7	−0·2	+1·1	6·0	− 5·1	− 1·3	2·8	16
February	3·3	+0·9	8·0	0·6	−0·2	+1·4	5·0	− 4·3	1·6	2·8	18
March	4·7	−0·1	9·5	− 0·4	−0·2	+0·2	5·0	− 7·2	2·5	2·5	13
April	7·7	−0·6	14·4	1·9	1·6	+0·2	7·0	− 4·8	4·6	3·7	7
May	11·7	+0·3	18·1	6·2	3·7	−0·4	6·8	− 2·6	7·7	3·0	2
June	15·8	+1·9	21·5	11·0	7·2	+0·2	11·0	1·9	11·5	3·4	0
July	13·1	−2·8	16·1	9·9	8·2	−0·9	11·8	5·7	10·6	2·9	0
August	14·1	−1·4	22·3	10·3	8·7	−0·1	12·0	5·5	11·4	2·8	0
September	12·5	+0·2	18·0	8·3	7·7	+0·6	11·2	1·7	10·1	2·2	0
October	9·3	+0·2	12·3	4·7	5·5	+0·8	8·7	− 1·7	7·4	2·4	4
November	5·0	−0·9	9·6	− 1·4	0·6	−1·2	4·9	− 7·0	2·8	2·2	11
December	6·5	+2·1	10·0	1·2	2·8	+2·2	8·0	− 1·8	4·7	2·1	2
YEAR	8.9	0.0	22·3	− 1·4	3.8	+0.3	12·0	− 7·2	6·4	2·7	73

Table 2 Monthly Temperatures (Ochil Hills, Carim) 1988

Stirling

Month	Total Precipitation	Percentage of Average	Percent of Accum. Average	Greatest fall in 24 hours Amount mm	Greatest fall in 24 hours Date	Precip. Recorded	0·2mm or more	1·0mm or more	5·0mm or more
January	131.9	128.8	128.8	25·4	18th	26	25	21	11
February	75·2	137·7	131·9	17·8	2nd	19	15	11	7
March	91.2	112·7	125.4	25.0	15th	21	19	15	5
April	73.2	176·4	133·0	26·2	18th	19	19	13	4
May	71·7	113·8	129·4	16·7	1st	17	16	9	5
June	14·7	27·7	115·8	7·8	25th	9	7	3	1
July	201·3	310·6	143·2	25·5	1st	29	29	23	17
August	132·4	189·1	149·3	23·5	13th	22	20	19	7
September	78·2	80·5	138·6	13·7	1st	16	15	13	6
October	126·5	134·1	138·0	21·2	25th	22	22	17	8
November	57·4	53·8	127·2	18·5	29th	9	8	7	4
December	52·9	53·6	119·4	14·2	3rd	18	15	10	3
Year	1106·6	119·4	–	26·2	18/4	227	210	161	78

Table 3. Monthly Precipitation (Stirling: Parkhead) 1988

Carim

Month	Total Precipitation	Percentage of Average	Percent of Accum Average
January	221.9	144.2	144.2
February	124.4	159.9	149.5
March	154.8	94.9	126.9
April	101.1	148.5	130.1
May	84.1	76.0	119.6
June	19.7	27.2	109.3
July	230.0	265.6	127.7
August	176.6	139.5	129.5
September	144.5	86.9	122.6
October	191.2	109.3	120.7
November	100.2	72.9	115.7
December	162.4	88.4	112.4
Year	1710.9	112.4	–

Table 4. Monthly Precipitation (Ochil Hills, Carim) 1988 (Based on Weekly Totals)

	Mean Maximum °C	Highest Maximum	Lowest Maximum	Mean Minimum °C	Highest Minimum	Lowest Minimum	Mean °C	Precipitation mm	Greatest Fall in 24 hours Amount mm	Greatest Fall in 24 hours Date
January	7.4	11.8	3.4	0.9	6.2	−4.0	4.1	–	–	–
February	8.7	14.0	3.6	1.3	5.9	−4.8	5.0	–	–	–
March	10.4	15.5	5.3	1.6	7.6	−6.1	6.0	–	–	–
April	13.4	20.5	6.6	3.8	9.6	−3.8	8.6	–	–	–
May	17.4	22.7	11.0	5.5	9.2	0.1	11.4	75.6	30.2	29
June	21.7	28.0	16.8	9.8	13.5	5.8	15.7	9.7	7.2	25
July	18.8	23.2	13.5	10.1	16.1	5.8	14.5	198.1	25.5	1
August	19.7	28.1	15.7	10.3	14.8	5.2	15.0	137.6	28.3	13
September	17.7	23.6	14.0	8.2	14.5	−0.8	12.9	84.6	15.2	1
October	13.4	18.7	10.1	5.3	11.5	−4.2	9.3	126.7	23.5	25
November	9.4	13.7	4.2	0.5	7.1	−5.9	5.0	59.4	15.7	29
December	10.3	14.2	3.6	3.9	10.3	−0.7	7.1	54.9	15.2	3.25
YEAR	14.0	28.1	3.4	5.1	16.1	−6.1	9.6	–	–	–

Table 5 Temperature and precipitation data for Bridge of Allan (Westerlea Drive) 1988

	Air Frost	Precipitation				Snow Lying at 0900	Snow Fall 09-09	Fog at 0900	Thunder Heard 09-09
		Recorded	0.2mm or more	1.0mm or more	5.0mm or more				
January	12	–	–	–	–	5	3	2	0
February	8	–	–	–	–	3	4	1	0
March	9	–	–	–	–	5	0	0	0
April	4	–	–	–	–	1	0	1	0
May	0	14	13	4	4	0	0	4	1
June	0	5	4	1	1	0	0	3	0
July	0	28	28	17	17	0	0	0	2
August	0	21	21	9	9	0	0	1	2
September	1	16	15	5	5	0	0	0	2
October	5	21	20	9	9	0	0	4	0
November	12	15	12	4	4	1	5	4	0
December	3	16	13	3	3	0	0	0	0
YEAR	54	–	–	–	–	15	12	20	7

NUMBER OF DAYS

Table 6 Weather frequencies for Bridge of Allan (Westerlea Drive) 1988

Stirling

	Maximum Temperature °C	Minimum Temperature °C	Soil Temperature (0.3m at 09.00) °C	Total Precipitation mm
January	5.8	0.0	2.7	102.4
February	6.2	0.4	2.5	54.6
March	8.5	1.5	4.3	80.9
April	11.6	3.1	7.5	41.5
May	14.9	5.5	11.4	63.0
June	17.4	8.3	14.7	53.0
July	19.6	10.7	16.6	64.8
August	19.1	9.9	16.2	70.0
September	15.9	8.2	13.6	97.2
October	12.6	5.2	10.1	94.3
November	8.8	2.4	6.2	106.7
December	7.1	1.5	3.9	98.6
YEAR	12.3	4.8	9.1	926.9

Table 7 Climatological Averages for Stirling (Parkhead) 1971-1988

Carim

	Maximum Temperature	Minimum Temperature	Total Precipitation mm
January	2.4	-1.3	153.9
February	2.4	-1.6	77.8
March	4.8	0.0	163.2
April	8.3	1.4	68.1
May	11.4	4.1	110.7
June	13.9	7.0	72.4
July	15.9	9.1	86.6
August	15.5	8.8	126.6
September	12.3	7.1	166.2
October	9.1	4.7	174.9
November	5.9	1.8	137.4
December	4.4	0.6	183.8
YEAR	8.9	3.5	1521.7

Table 8 Climatological Averages for Ochil Hills (Carim) 1981-88

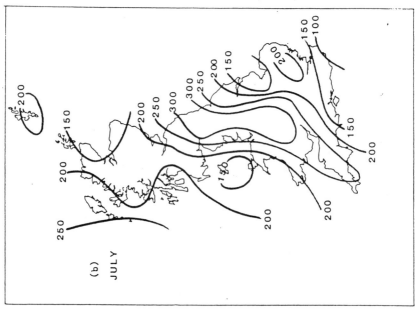

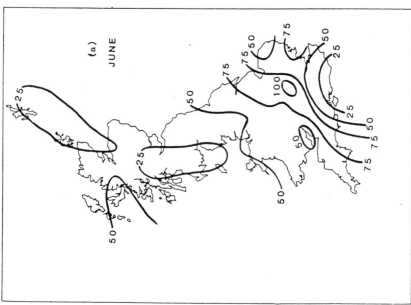

Figure 1 Percentage of normal rainfall (from COL Bulletin)

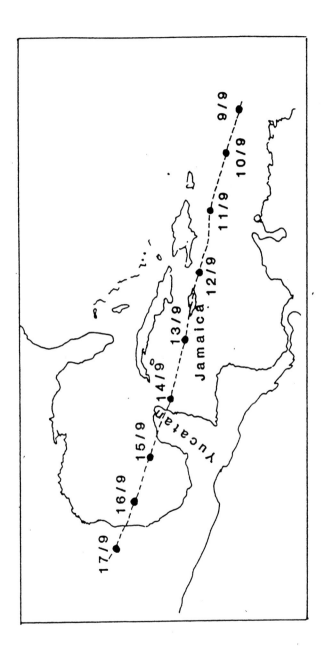

Figure 2 The Progress of Hurricane Gilbert September 1988

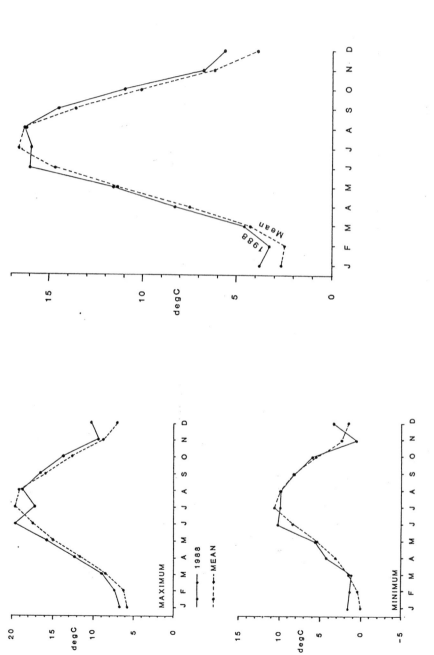

Figure 4 Soil temperatures

Stirling (Parkhead) 1988

Figure 3 Air temperatures

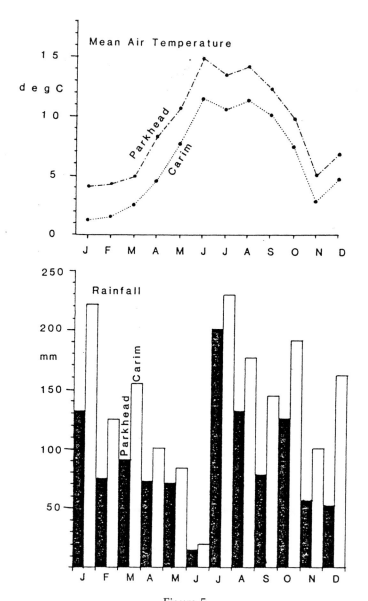

Figure 5
Comparison between Stirling (Parkhead) and Ochil Hills (Carim) 1988

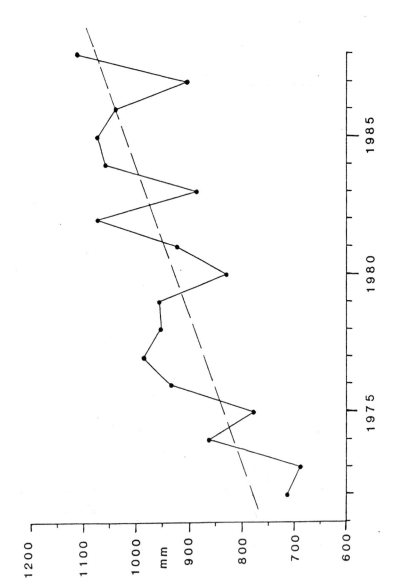

Figure 6   Trend in annual rainfall totals at Stirling (Parkhead) 1972-1988

BOOK REVIEW

LIVING WITH WILDLIFE. David Stephen.
Canongate. 1989. 178pp. hbk. ISBN 0 86241 215 8. £14.95.

David Stephen was asked to write this book to commemorate 150 years of the Scottish Society for the Prevention of Cruelty to Animals, and this delightful feast of words and photographs has been handsomely produced by Canongate.

How fortunate we are that all but two chapters, seals and garden birds, of this material had been prepared before his death — sadly and unexpectedly — on 22nd January 1989. Only two months before at our Man and the Landscape symposium he had helped us with the competition for the Young Forth Naturalist Awards, and presented the prizes in suitably impressive style to the groups of youngsters from the winning primary schools. As the Preface says "in the sad days following his death it has become clear that . . . the book had become a testament to his life and to his beliefs."

We have here 170 pages full of the intimate detail of closely observed wildlife, so knowledgeably written and superbly photographed observations by this fascinating man; *muy simpatico* as his Spanish friends might have said; and as James Seaton says in his Scotsman obituary "David Stephen was a magisterial writer — his natural history can be taken for granted, the writing is revelatory."

In addition to this fine book we look forward to whatever 'memorial' is being planned to bear his name.

L. Corbett

Editorial Notes — Young Forth Environmentalist

From this year 1990 we are modifying the Young Forth Naturalist competition for compatibility with the broader environmental field and the activities of more of the members of the Central Region Environmental Education Forum. Tom Weir has kindly agreed to present the awards to winning schools on Saturday 17th November at the 16th Man and the Landscape symposium — whose theme this year is Loch Lomond (see p114).

Prizes are again donated by Bank of Scotland.

BOOK REVIEWS

ANNALS OF A COUNTRY PARISH. William B. Maclaren.
Falkirk District Libraries and Museums. 1989. 77pp.
ISBN 0 906586 56 9. £2 (plus 60p p&p by post).

The title page further clarifies this with ''a fascinating picture of old days and ways in Bothkennar parish — a complete transcript of the session minutes. . . ''.

The retired former minister of Bothkennar Church goes on in his preface to explain how his original intent of a selective popular work based on these records of 1722-1741 was changed to providing a true transcript for the benefit of students and all directly or indirectly concerned with Scottish history, plus an introduction to the history of the locality, and with notes and other helpful comments on the minutes themselves.

And fascinating it is. Arrangements for celebrating the Lord's Supper in April 1725 include the duties of heritors and others to provide tokens for the 800 participants, grounds reserved outwith the church to accommodate this number and an especially constructed open air tent (a roofed pulpit), tables, and all necessary furnishings — silver cups and plate, pewter, flagons. . . . The glossary under 'tent' comments — ''see Burn's Holy Fair which deals with the abuses that arose''. The marital and other behaviours of the times and society's attentions to and advices on these are well illustrated in these records and comments.

L. Corbett

SCOTTISH FAMILY HISTORY. David Moody.
Batsford, 1989. 219pp. ppbk ISBN 0 7134 572 28. £9.95.
hbk 0 7134 572 44. £14.95.

This is a companion to the author's highly acclaimed *Scottish Local History: An Introductory Guide*. His approach for family history goes well beyond genealogy or even biography, although he devotes a chapter to each. The theme is the reconstruction of family life rather than simply of a family tree, noting that genealogy often attracts enthusiasts without training and without an historical education to understand the context in which their ancestors lived, worked and died.

The book is both an appeal and a guide to anyone seriously interested in this field to develop a much more thorough understanding of the sources *and* of the times through which the subjects lived. The range of materials itemised and explained is formidable. It should be of immense value to both beginners and experienced practitioners. Whether it will have an impact in the future remains to be seen.

B. J. Elliott

CENTRAL REGION BIRD REPORT 1988

C. J. Henty
University of Stirling

This report covers the Central Region excluding Loch Lomondside and parts of Stirling District west of the River Endrick. The provisional checklist mentioned in the last report has been circulated and some useful comments have come back. There has been a delay on progress to publication since it has become apparent that its condensed format should be translated into a fuller written form, and this will take some time. Further information is still urgently needed for the two parts of the area that have only recently come into the scope of these reports. The first is the highland area in the northern part of Central Region — the Ben Lui massif and the little visited hills between Glen Dochart and Glen Lochay. The second is in the extreme southeast of Central Region, where the coastal stretch from Bo'ness to Blackness has been allocated to us out of the old county of West Lothian. In the present report there are several items arising from work done during the continuing national survey of breeding birds. The editor/recorder hopes that people contributing to this study will not overlook the extraction of appropriate records for this report. Since the northwest sector of our area covers the zone of hybridisation between Carrion and Hooded Crows, it would be valuable to collect records of the relative frequencies of pure black, apparently pure Hoodie type (with pale grey backs and bellies) and hybrids with either dark grey backs and bellies or these areas intermixed with black. I say 'apparently pure Hoodie' since there is a pale type of hybrid very like a Hoodie except that the tail coverts are dark, but it would take a good view to see this.

The building up of the dams at Carron Valley Reservoir has, during 1988, been followed by a permanent raising of the water level and failure of the wintering Bean Geese to appear at this, their original, locality; the breeding populations of waders have apparently also been affected. A new species for Central Region was a drake Red Crested Pochard on Gartmorn Dam, subject to the proviso that wildfowl are particularly likely to be escapes from captivity. There were particularly large flocks of Great Crested Grebes at Kinneil which at times concealed a Red-necked Grebe and the second Ruddy Duck for the region. In the birds of prey there is a notable spring record of Marsh Harrier at Tullibody Inch and it seems that Buzzards are attempting to breed in the southeast of Falkirk District. Less encouraging is the news that in the west a Golden Eagle was shot on the nest. Early in the autumn there was a strong passage of Curlew Sandpipers on the Forth estuary and later in the year many Guillemots appeared, however they did not this year get wrecked inland to any extent. Corn Buntings seem to be holding on to their breeding toehold in the east of Falkirk District whilst elsewhere there were brief spring visits from Lesser Whitethroat and Red-backed Shrike. Finally, late in the year Waxwings appeared in at least four localities, but there were no large numbers as have appeared in the eastern half of Scotland.

The following observers, noted by initials, contributed to this 1988 list — R. A. Broad, D. M. Bryant, M. V. Bell, W. R. Brackenridge, C. Crawford, J. Crook, Nature Conservancy Council, A. Henty, C. J. Henty, D. C. Jardine, D. Matthews, J. Mitchell, A. S. Moore, S. F. Newton, R. K. Pollock, H. Robb, R. J. Ruffell, P. Stirling-Aird, P. D. Taylor, D. Thorogood, M. Trubridge, J. Wheeler, I. Wilson, A. Wood.

Falkirk and Clackmannan Districts are indicated by the marginal F and C, S refers to the old Stirling County part of Stirling District and SWP refers to the Perth part of Stirling District.

SYSTEMATIC LIST

RED-THROATED DIVER *Gavia stellata*
F   1 Bo'ness 3rd December and 1 Grangemouth on 11th (PDT MVB)
SWP   All records probably refer to one pair: Pair Loch F 22nd April but not later. Pair Loch D 8th and 18th May, single on 7th June. None Loch E 3rd June but pair with 2 small young on 27th; 2 large young 27th July, solitary juvenile 15th August — both thought to have fledged (JC MT) (in 1987 pair at Loch E 11th June with empty nest, none on 2nd July)

BLACK—THROATED DIVER *Gavia arctica*
F   1 Bo'ness 17th January, 1 Grangemouth 13th November (DMB)
SWP   First at Loch A, a pair 31st March, bird sitting 4th May; site visited 17th May — no eggs but a freshly dead male bird found, death due to bacterial septicaemia; 2 birds seen 26th May to 28th June, singles 24th July and 21st August. 1 Loch C 3rd May; pair Loch G 6th May; 1 Loch F 13th May and pair on 28th (MT JC)

LITTLE GREBE *Tachybaptus ruficollis*
C   3 Gartmorn Dam 17th January (MVB)
S   First at Airthrey 11th February, 5 pairs, only 11 young fledged from at least 11 nesting attempts; still 2 on 13th December (MVB)
SWP   Adult + 1 young Loch Ard 26th July (JC)

GREAT CRESTED GREBE *Podiceps cristatus*
        693 Forth estuary 17th January (DMB et al)

F   Kinneil: 470 on 17th January and 110 on 31st, 118 on 21st February. 230 on 16th July and 48 on 20th, 180 on 14th August and 310 on 31st; 250 on 22nd October, 100 on 20th November (DMB MVB DCJ DT)

C   4 Gartmorn Dam 17th January and 6 on 20th November (MVB WRB)

S   7 pairs in summer Carron Valley Reservoir (AW), only 10 there on 21st August (DT)

SWP   2 pairs Lake of Menteith. First at Loch Watston 21st February and 2 on 27th March. Pair Blairdrummond (new pit) 17th April (WRB DT)

RED-NECKED GREBE *Podiceps grisegena*
F   1 Kinneil 18th August (DCJ)

FULMAR *Fulmar glacialis*
F   2 Kinneil 14th August and 1 on 31st (DT)

GANNET *Sula bassana*
SWP   Immature found dead Glengyle 23rd February (RAB)

CORMORANT *Phalacrocorax carbo*
F   210 flying W Kinneil 10th January; 160 Grangemouth 29th December (DJC). 66 Skinflats 6th September and 160 on 11th December (MVB)

C   184 Kennetpans 17th January, 230 on 30th December (MVB SFN). At South Alloa roost: 134 on 6th February, 86 on 21st and 97 on 24th, 95 on 6th March; 120 on 24th September (CJH)

S   At Airthrey 1 from 31st March to 19th April, 2 on 25th April; 1 on 17th June and 16th September (MVB)

GREY HERON *Ardea cinerea*
F   13 Skinflats 17th January and 15 on 8th September (MVB)

MUTE SWAN *Cygnus olor*
     71 Forth estuary 12th December (DMB et al)
     Successful breeding known at two sites in Clackmannan and five in Stirling District with no breeding or inadequate data at a further seven sites. No nests known on canals in Falkirk District (DM)

F   Pair with 2 young E Grangemouth 8th August and 2 adults Kinneil (SFN)

S   Pair at Airthrey hatched 7, fledged 5 (MVB)

C   Pair Alva Pools, failed (SFN)

SWP   Pair at Doune Ponds hatched 6, fledged 4 (WRB)

BEWICK'S SWAN *Cygnus bewickii*
SWP   2 Drip 7th February (WRB)

WHOOPER SWAN *Cygnus cygnus*
F   22 flying W Bo'ness and Kinneil 20th November (DT PDT)
C   14 Alva 2nd January and 28 Menstrie on 16th (CJH DT). 1
        juvenile Alva 13th September and 16 in stubble 10th November
        (SFN), 14 (1 juvenile) Menstrie 12th November and 10
        Gartmorn Dam on 19th, 71 (15 juveniles) Alva 31st December
        (CJH PDT SFN)
S   9 Carron Valley Reservoir 14th January (DCJ)
SWP   70 Drip 7th February and 78 on 14th, 55 there 28th when also
        26 Thornhill; 51 on 27th March, last 39 on 1st April (MVB WRB
        DT). 6 Loch Dhu-Chon 16th January and 10 from 23rd February
        to 26th March; 3 Loch Achray and 8 Loch Venachar 24th
        January (DT MT).
        First were 2 Ashfield 30th September, 1 Loch Macanrie 19th
        October and 51 Thornhill on 30th (WRB RAB DT). The Drip
        (Chalmerston) herd included only 1 juvenile to 117 adults on
        12th and 18th December but another group on the 18th had
        10 juveniles to 62 adults; 152 on 5th November plus 5 at
        Thornhill (DT RAB). 23 Kinbuck 12th November (MVB)

BEAN GOOSE *Anser fabalis*
F   105 Loch Elrig 21st February, feeding in heather to east of loch
        (DCJ)

PINK-FOOTED GOOSE *Anser brachyrhynchus*
F   Skinflats: 330 on 14th February, 160 on 5th April, 500 on 20th
        November and 11th December (MVB WRB DT)
C   74 E Dollar 2nd May. First at Alva 13th September (SFN). 210
        high S Cambus (from over Ochils) 11.30 19th November (CJH)
S   1500 Kippen 10th January. 70 NW Bridge of Allan at 13.00 on
        21st February. 400 Arnprior 12th April, flights to N at Airthrey
        26th and 27th April (CJH SFN DT IW). Flights to SE over
        Stirling in mid November. 37 W Airthrey 09.54 15th December
        (CJH DT)
SWP   2000 Blairdrummond 27th March; 5000 Lake of Menteith 5th
        April, 3612 Carse of Stirling on 17th, 950 Blairdrummond on
        24th. 120 N Ashfield 24th April (RAB WRB MVB DT).
        First over Doune 13th September. 1200 Thornhill 12th
        November and 1350 on 18th (WRB RAB DT). 6500 at dawn
        flight Loch Mahaick 12th November (SFN)

WHITE-FRONTED GOOSE *Anser albifrons*
SWP   1 (Greenland form) Aberfoyle 17th April (RAB)

GREYLAG GOOSE *Anser anser*
F   19 Loch Elrig 16th January and 16 on 12th March (DCJ)
C   60 N Longcarse 17.00 on 6th February (CJH)
S   50 N at Bridge of Allan 20th November (CJH)
SWP   Low numbers — 400 roosting Loch Venachar 13th November
         and total of 118 on Carse of Stirling on 18th (RAB WRB)

BARNACLE GOOSE *Branta leucopsis*
SWP   4 Thornhill 12th November (1 Loch Watston 30th October
         maybe escape) (DT)

BRENT GOOSE *Branta bernicla*
F   7, pale bellied form, Skinflats 8th, 9th and 10th September
         (MVB RAB DT)

SHELDUCK *Tadorna tadorna*
         2244 Forth estuary 8th September (DMB et al)
F   Skinflats: 434 on 17th January, 465 on 14th February, 300 on
         27th August, 585 on 8th September, 432 on 11th December
         (MVB WRB). 2400 (moult flock) 16th August and 1579 Kinneil
         8th September (DMB SFN). 240 Bo'ness 6th November (CJH)
C   2 pairs Cambus in April (WRB). 85 Tullibody Inch and 70 Alloa
         Inch 6th March; 115 Alloa Inch 24th September (CJH)

WIGEON *Anas penelope*
         586 Forth estuary 12th December (DMB et al)
C   440 Gartmorn Dam 17th January (MVB)
S   34 Loch Coulter 17th December — high count for site (WB).
         1 Airthrey 31st August (DMB)
SWP   20 Lake of Menteith 24th December — high count for site (RAB)

GADWALL *Anas strepera*
F   1 Skinflats (Bothkenna) 5th April (RAB)

TEAL *Anas crecca*
         1843 Forth estuary 8th September (DMB et al)
F   1764 Kinneil 17th January and 1825 on 8th September (DMB
         SFN)
C   190 Gartmorn Dam 17th January (MVB). 110 Cambus 19th
         November (CJH).
         First at breeding localities in Ochils 12th April, 4 males Upper
         Glendevon 16th May (SFN)
S   88 Touch Reservoir 15th January (CC). 11 Airthrey 26th
         October an alltime record (DMB)

MALLARD *Anas platyrhynchos*
         1563 Forth estuary 8th September (DMB et al)

F   Skinflats: 485 on 17th January and 650 on 8th September (MVB)

C   900 Gartmorn Dam 17th January (MVB). 2 broods Cambus (WRB)

S   425 Touch Reservoir 15th January, 110 Kippen Muir 9th September, 115 Loch Laggan 12th November, 98 Loch Coulter 13th November (WRB DT CC). Max at Airthrey on 270 on 7th January and 378 on 22nd August, 21 broods but only 41 fledged (MVB)

SWP   174 Lake of Menteith 14th January (RAB). Female with 4 small young on puddle at Lecropt 1st October (CJH)

PINTAIL *Anas acuta*

F   Skinflats: 52 on 31st January, 35 on 14th February; 46 on 19th November, 61 on 11th and 29th December (MVB DCJ PDT). Kinneil: Pair on 22nd April, male on 4th and 10th May; 5 on 8th September, 16 on 22nd October, 41 on 13th November (DCJ SFN). 56 Grangemouth 20th November (DMB)

SHOVELER *Spatula clypeata*

F   3 Kinneil 22nd October (DCJ). 10 Grangemouth 16th August and 13th November (DMB)

C   13 Cambus 20th August (WRB)

S   1 Airthrey 25th August and 26th October (DMB)

SWP   1 Loch Macanrie 18th October (RAB)

RED-CRESTED POCHARD *Netta rufina*

C   Male Gartmorn Dam 10th January (DCJ) (First record for Central Region, however it is always uncertain whether records of this species are due to birds escaped from captivity, Editor)

POCHARD *Aythya ferina*

F   1 Kinneil 8th May (DCJ)

C   42 Gartmorn Dam 17th January (MVB)

SWP   22 Loch Watson 21st February (DT), 8 Loch Chon 27th February (RAB)

TUFTED DUCK *Aythya fuligula*

C   60 Gartmorn Dam 17th January (MVB). Pair Alva Pools 27th April-2nd May; 9 on River Devon at Alva 10th December (SFN)

S   Max at Airthrey 61 on 11th February and 66 on 13th December, c10 pairs bred — 2 early broods fledged 16 young, rest failed in mid-June during good weather (MVB). 26 North Third Reservoir 13th November (WRB)

SCAUP *Aythya marila*

F   Kinneil: 4 on 1st January, 3 on 8th May and 2 on 10th (DCJ).

7 females at sewage outfall Bo'ness 3rd December (PDT)

EIDER *Somateria mollissima*
F   2 Grangemouth 12th June (DCJ); 3 males Blackness 6th November (CJH)

LONG-TAILED DUCK *Clangula hyemalis*
S   Male Kippen Muir 22nd October (DT)

VELVET SCOTER *Melanitta fusca*
F   2 Blackness 6th November (CJH)

GOLDENEYE *Bucephala clangula*
    165 Forth estuary 17th January (DMB et al)
F   157 Bo'ness (Carriden) 3rd December (PDT). Scarce Skinflats — 1 on 17th January (MVB)
C   39 Gartmorn Dam 17th January (MVB). 1 Alva 1oth-25th November (SFN)
S   Male Airthrey 26th October (DMB)

RED-BREASTED MERGANSER *Mergus serrator*
    137 Forth estuary 21st of February (DMB et al)
F   45 Skinflats 14th February and 37 on 11th December (MVB). 48 Blackness 6th November (CJH)
C   82 Kennetpans 30th December (SFN)
S   Female and 6 large young Cambuskenneth 4th August (IW)

GOOSANDER *Mergus merganser*
F   2 Skinflats 29th December (DCJ)
C   8 (2 males) Upper Glendevon Reservoir 16th May (SFN); brood 6 Rumbling Bridge, 24th May. 3 Alva September-December (SFN)
S   14 Loch Laggan 21st February and 12 on 13th March (DT)
SWP   19 Glensherup Reservoir 6th April, 25 Castlehill Reservoir on 2nd, 16 on 12th and 18 on 28th November. Brood 7 (well grown) Frandy early July (DMB SFN IW)
    Pair Loch Ard 3rd May and 6 (2 males) on 27th July. 7 (6 males) Loch Chon 18th May, female Loch Katrine 9th June (JC)

RUDDY DUCK *Oxyura jamaicensis*
F   Male Kinneil 21st February, offshore with Great Crested Grebes (DCJ)

MARSH HARRIER *Circus aeruginosus*
C   Female/immature Tullibody Inch 2nd May, quartered reedbeds, several feathers missing from tail (CC)

HEN HARRIER *Circus cyaneus*
C Ringtail Balquharn Burn (Ochils) 9th June (SFN)
SWP Pair bred Trossachs (MT); male Thornhill 12th November (DT), 1 Sheriffmuir 15th July (2nd summer male) and 1 on 10th September (MVB)

SPARROWHAWK *Accipiter nisus*
 Records from Bo'ness, Falkirk, Slamannan, Stirling, Cambuskenneth, Bridge of Allan, Sheriffmuir, Loch Ard and Achray Forests (WRB JC CJH PDT). 1 skimming pavement in middle of Stirling (IW)

BUZZARD *Buteo buteo*
F 1 possibly with occupied nest Muiravonside 13th June (JW), bird not seen later (A. Maciver); (no proven breeding record known for Falkirk District, Editor)
C 1 Gartmorn Dam 17th January; 2 Dollar 2nd April, 3 Alva 31st May (SFN DT)
S 3 Touch House and 1 Scout Head 12th March (CJH)
SWP Pair Cromlix in June, pair Doune (4 seen November), 4 Sheriffmuir 26th November (WRB)

GOLDEN EAGLE *Aquila chrysaetos*
SWP Trossachs: of 2 pairs one fledged 1 young, the other produced 2 eggs but male was shot at nest (MT). Elsewhere in region birds present at 3 of 4 home ranges (PSA). 1 Ben Challum 14th January, 1 Meall Ghaordie 15th August, 1 mobbed by Hooded Crows Stob a'Choin 23rd April, pair and 2 juveniles Trossachs 24th September and 3 on 27th (WRB DM)

OSPREY *Pandion haliaetus*
 First record of spring 2 on 5th May, last 1 Loch Ard 12th August (IW WRB)

MERLIN *Falco columbarius*
F 1 Kinneil 12th December (DMB)
C Female Menstrie 20th April and Glendevon on 24th (SFN)
S 1 St Ninian's 23rd November (WRB)
SWP 1 Loch Arklett 12th April (IW)

PEREGRINE *Falco peregrinus*
 In Central Region 24 territories checked, 21 pairs and one single bird; 16 successful pairs raised 33 young (PSA JM et al). A Trossachs pair failed when eggs were broken during incubation (MT)
F 1 Loch Elrig 21st February (DCJ); 1 Bo'ness 20th November (PDT)

C   2 Muckhart 10th April (DMB)
S   1 mobbing Ravens North Third Reservoir 13th November (WRB)
SWP   1 Lecropt 10th and 13th January (WRB MVB). 1 Kirkton Glen 17th April, 1 Gleneagles 28th November (IW)

RED GROUSE *Lagopus lagopus*
C   Scarce on tops of Ochils (SFN)
SWP   Good numbers Glen Lochay (e.g. 10 Meall Ghaordie 20th December); only a few pairs Strathfillan-Ben Challum 14th January (WRB)

PTARMIGAN *Lagopus mutus*
SWP   2 Ben Challum 14th January (WRB), 2 at 800m Stob a'Choin 12th June, 4 at 900m Ben More 15th October, not seen during Atlas visits to Cruach Ardrain and Beinn Tulaichean 15th May and 3rd July (DM)

BLACK GROUSE *Tetrao tetrix*
C   Female at 380m Kirk Crags (Tillicoultry) 20th May (SFN)

CAPERCAILLIE
SWP   Male displaying Drumore Wood 29th April (Foresters report several males and females Duke's Pass) (WRB)

WATER RAIL *Rallus aquaticus*
SWP   1 Loch Watston 30th October (DT)

CORNCRAKE *Crex crex*
F   Calling near Denny 24th June to 17th July (per RAB)

MOORHEN *Gallinula chloropus*
C   3 pairs Cambus (WRB). Probably increased on River Devon at Alva (SFN)
S   12 pairs at Airthrey reared at least 21 young (one pair did not nest), much fighting with Coots; on wildfowl counts up to 21 noted January to March, max 39 on 16th September with 28 or less through rest of autumn (MVB)
SWP   2 pairs Doune Ponds, 4 wintered Ashfield early in year and 3 in December (WRB)

COOT *Fulica atra*
C   3 pairs Cambus (WRB). 280 Gartmorn Dam 17th January (MVB)
S   At Airthrey 27 pairs made 35 nesting at attempts and fledged 61 young (4 pairs failed to rear any and one was double brooded); a late nest hatched on 5th September but the two

young died within a month. Counts in non-breeding season very uniform with maxima of 83 on 11th February and 79 on 14th November (MVB)

SWP   3 pairs Doune Ponds (WRB). 282 Lake of Monteith 14th January (RAB)

OYSTERCATCHER *Haematopus ostralegus*

925 Forth estuary 21st February (DMB et al)

C   First Alva 2nd March; clutch found Glendevon 24th April (SFN)

SWP   1st Ashfield 13th February, Dunblane on 15th (WRB MVB), 60 Loch Watston 21st February and 100 on 27th March (DT)

S   1 Kippen Muir 21st February (DT)

LITTLE RINGED PLOVER *Charadrius dubius*

F   1 Kinneil 16th August (DMB)

RINGED PLOVER *Charadrius hiaticula*

54 Forth estuary 8th September (DMB et al)

F   18 Grangemouth 11th June (DJC); 11 Bo'ness 8th September (SFN)

C   1 Upper Glendevon Reservoir 16th May (SFN). 5 Cambus 30th June (WRB)

S   2 Pairs Lower Earlsburn Reservoir 2nd April (DT), 4 pairs at Carron Valley Reservoir (AW)

GOLDEN PLOVER *Pluvialis apricaria*

300 Forth estuary 8th September (DMB et al)

F   200 Blackness 6th November (CJH). Skinflats: 175 on 14th February, 180 on 6th April, 100 on 8th September, 130 on 1st October and 490 on 22nd (MVB DCJ)

C   Pair Ben Cleuch at 610m 26th May (SFN). 35 Cambus 19th November (CJH)

SWP   2 pairs Ben Challuim 12th June (WRB)

GREY PLOVER *Pluvialis squatarola*

8 (only) Forth estuary 12th December (DMB et al)

F   85 Skinflats 2nd October and 12 on 19th November (DCJ PDT)

LAPWING *Vanellus vanellus*

2315 Forth estuary 8th September (DMB et al)

F   500 Kinneil 22nd October and 289 on 11th December. 530 Skinflats 30th September (DCJ SFN)

C   320 Longcarse 24th September and 1200 Tullibody Inch on 25th, 370 Alva 7th October, 550 Cambus 19th November (WRB CJH SFN)

SWP   2 pairs at Keir roundabout, decreasing at Ashfield (WRB)

KNOT *Calidris canutus*
  6540 Forth estuary 12th December (DMB et al)
F   100 Skinflats 11th December (MVB). Kinneil: 1200 on 10th January and 1500 on 30th. 10 on 14th August, 600 on 2nd November and 1000 on 20th, 2000 on 10th December and 6023 on 11th (RAB DCJ SFN DT PDT)

SANDERLING *Calidris alba*
F   1 Grangemouth 11th June; 10 Kinneil 14th August (DCJ)

LITTLE STINT *Calidris minuta*
F   1 Skinflats 16th August and 2 on 28th, 1 on 3rd and 9th September. 3 Grangemouth 31st August; 12 Kinneil 3rd September and 17 on 8th (RAB DMB MVB DCJ SFN DT)

CURLEW SANDPIPER *Calidris ferruginea*
  75 Forth estuary 8th September (DMB et al)
F   4 Skinflats 27th August, 10 on 3rd September and 46 on 9th, 1 on 12th November (RAB WRB DCJ DT). 12 Kinneil 3rd September and 20 on 10th; 50 Grangemouth 31st August, 64 on 8th September and 61 on 10th; 80 Kincardine Bridge 10th September (RAB DMB MVB)

DUNLIN *Calidris alpina*
  3017 Forth estuary 12th December (DMB)
F   Skinflats: 1720 on 17th January and 1770 on 14th February; 730 on 8th September and 1500 on 30th, 1000 on 22nd October, 1585 on 11th December (MVB DCJ). 1232 Kinneil 11th December (SFN)
C   5 Cambus 30th June (WRB). A pair at Carron Valley Reservoir in summer but no proof of breeding (AW)

RUFF *Philomachus pugnax*
F   4 Kinneil 31st August and 14 on 10th September; 4 Grangemouth 16th August and 6 on 31st, 19 on 8th September; Skinflats: 5 on 3rd September, 9 on 9th and 8 on 10th; 1 on 12th and 19th November (MVB DMB DCJ DT PDT RAB)

JACK SNIPE *Lymnocryptes minimus*
F   Kinneil: 1 on 1st January and 5 on 17th, 6 on 13th March, 4 on 6th and 2 on 11th April and 1 on 22nd (DCJ). 1 on 15th October, 2 on 11th November and 4 on 13th, 11 on 10th December (RAB CJH DCJ)
S   2 Cambuskenneth 22nd November (IW)
SWP   1 at Doune Ponds 12th February, 1 on 14th December (WRB)

SNIPE *Gallinago gallinago*

F   Kinneil: 15 on 10th January, 23 on 6th April and 9 on 11th. 21 on 12th September, 26 on 1st and 31 on 22nd October, 45 on 2nd and 13th November (RAB DCJ). 15 Skinflats 9th September (DT)

C   12 Cambus 20th August and 28th September, 6 on 19th November (WRB CJH IW)

S   3 pairs Carron Valley Reservoir (AW)

SWP   10 Doune Ponds 14th December (WRB)

WOODCOCK *Scolopax rusticola*

November records from Loch Laggan, Torrie Forest and 2 roosting together in Holly bush in Mine Wood (WRB CJH DT)

BLACK-TAILED GODWIT *Limosa limosa*

30 Forth estuary 8th September (DMB et al)

F   Kinneil: 2 on 1st January, 8 on 4th May, 1 on 14th August and 9 on 31st, 27 on 8th September and 19 on 12th, 1 on 28th December. Grangemouth: 4 on 31st January, 5 on 18th August, 22 on 8th September and 18 on 13th November, 3 Skinflats 8th September (DMB MVB DCJ SFN DT)

C   2 Cambus 26th August, 3 Tullibody Inch 25th September (WRB)

BAR-TAILED GODWIT *Limosa lapponica*

397 Forth estuary 8th September (DMB et al)

F   Kinneil: 120 on 10th January, 50 on 22nd April and 6 on 4th May; 279 on 11th December (DCJ SFN). 100 Grangemouth on 1st September, 84 Skinflats 8th September (MVB DCJ)

WHIMBREL *Numenius phaeopus*

F   Kinneil: 2 on 20th July, 1 on 14th and 16th August, 4 on 31st August (DT). 2 Skinflats 31st August (DCJ)

S   1 NW at Airthrey 12th May (DMB)

CURLEW *Numenius arquata*

F   169 Skinflats 17th January and 416 on 8th September. 250 Kinneil 21st February and 430 on 11th December (MVB DCJ SFN)

SWP   7 SW (high) Dunblane 26th June — start of departure for moors (MVB)

SPOTTED REDSHANK *Tringa erythropus*

F   1 Grangemouth 16th August and 3 on 31st (DMB). Kinneil-Skinflats: 1 on 31st August, 5 on 8th September, 2 on 12th and 1 on 30th (RAB MVB DCJ SFN)

C   2 Longcarse 24th September, 1 Tullibody Inch on 25th (WRB
         CJH)

REDSHANK *Tringa totanus*
         3064 Forth estuary 8th September (DMB et al)
F   Skinflats: 1175 on 17th January and 945 on 14th February, 705
         on 8th September and 700 on 11th December (MVB). 300
         Grangemouth 10th January (WRB), 1236 Kinneil on 11th
         December (SFN)
C   Bred Cambus, adult feeding juvenile on 30th June (WRB); 25
         Longcarse 24th September (CJH)

GREENSHANK *Tringa nebularia*
F   1 Grangemouth 31st January and 11th December, 1 on 9th July.
         1 Skinflats 11th June; 2 on 16th, 27th and 31st August. Kinneil:
         1 on 22nd April; 1 on 14th and 31st August and 2 on 16th and
         18th, 2 on 3rd September and 7 on 8th (DMB MVB RAB DCJ
         SFN DT) (low numbers this autumn, Editor)
C   1 Longcarse 24th September and 1 Cambus on 25th (WRB CJH)

GREEN SANDPIPER *Tringa ochropus*
C   1 Cambus 26th August (WRB)
SWP   1 Doune Ponds 25th August (WRB)

COMMON SANDPIPER *Actitis hypoleucos*
F   5 Kinneil 20th July and 18th August (DCJ DT)
C   1 Muckhart 25th April (DMB). First at Alva 15th April, 2 pairs,
         young fledged 22nd June, last on 5th July. 7 pairs in May on
         Devon above Upper Glendevon Reservoir (SFN). 6 Cambus
         30th June (WRB)
SWP   Pair Doune ponds, first for 4 years (WRB)

TURNSTONE *Arenaria interpres*
         144 Forth estuary 8th September (DMB et al)
F   6 Skinflats 14th February, 1 Kinneil 14th August, 1
         Grangemouth 16th August, 4 Bo'ness 3rd September (MVB
         DCJ SFN DT)

POMARINE SKUA *Stercorarius pomarinus*
F   1 Bo'ness 3rd September (SFN), 5 Skinflats and 3 Kinneil 13rd
         November (DCJ DMB)

ARCTIC SKUA *Stercorarius parasiticus*
F   1 Grangemouth 13th November (DMB)

GREAT SKUA *Stercorarius skua*
F   1 Kinneil 1st October (DCJ)

BLACK-HEADED GULL *Larus ridibundus*
F   1500 Skinflats 12th November (DCJ)
C   Alva: 500 on 1st September, 1450 on 2nd October, 3650 in
         December (SFN)

COMMON GULL *Larus canus*
SWP   19 nest Loch Tinker 28th May (JC)

LESSER BLACK-BACKED GULL *Larus fuscus*
F   51 Skinflats 22nd October and 124 on 13th November (roosts).
         1 Kinneil 30th January (DCJ)
S   1 Stirling 24th January (DT)

HERRING GULL *Larus argentatus*
F   16,700 Skinflats roost 13th November (DCJ)
C   1400 Longcarse 24th February, soaring E at 17.35 (to roost)
         (CJH)

GREAT BLACK-BACKED GULL *Larus marinus*
F   183 Kinneil 28th December (DCJ)
C   16 Cambus 19th November (CJH)

KITTIWAKE *Rissa tridactyla*
F   31 flying upriver, Bo'ness 20th November (DT)

SANDWICH TERN *Sterna sandvicensis*
F   100 Skinflats 8th September (MVB)

COMMON TERN *Sterna hirundo*
F   110 Grangemouth mooring islands 22nd May — 60 apparently
         brooding at West Channel and 10 by River Carron (DM). 41
         occupied sites 9th July (DMB)
S   Present at Carron Valley Reservoir in summer, breeding
         uncertain (AW)

GUILLEMOT *Uria allge*
F   49 Skinflats 17th January, 8 on 12th November and 130 on 11th
         December. 1 Kinneil 1st October and 6 on 22nd; 300 Kincardine
         Bridge 19th November, 200 Grangemouth and 260 (mainly
         flying upstream) Bo'ness 20th November. Numbers decreased
         in December (DMB MVB DCJ DM DT). None found dead on
         Skinflats tideline on 4th January 1989 (DM)
C   7 Cambus and 1 Manor Powis 20th November and 2 on Devon
         at Alva on 25th (DMB WRB SFN)
S   5 Cambuskenneth 4th December (IW)
SWP   1 dead Lake of Menteith 24th December (RAB)

RAZORBILL *Alca torda*
F   2 Grangemouth 10th October (DCJ)

FERAL ROCK DOVE *Columba livia*
C   80 in stubble Longcarse 24th September (CJH)

STOCK DOVE *Columba oenas*
C   25 Longcarse 6th March (CJH), 23 Cambus 20th February (WRB). Max 5 Alva in April, prospecting hole, 3 there 22nd December. 1 Rumbling Bridge gorge 30th April (SFN)
SWP   2 Lake of Menteith 5th April. Pair on rocks at Loch Katrine 9th June (RAB JC)

WOOD PIGEON *Columba palumba*
C   700 Gartmorn 17th January (MVB), 2000 in stubble Menstrie 22nd December (SFN)
SWP   650 Lecropt 17th January and 200 on 15th June (MVB WRB)

COLLARED DOVE *Streptopelia decaocto*
S   14 Airthrey 13th January (MVB)

CUCKOO *Cuculus canorus*
C   1 Alva 29th April (SFN)
SWP   2 Menteith Hills 21st May (DT)

BARN OWL *Tyto alba*
F   1 over A801 near Union Canal (NS950777) at 21.15 on 20th March (JW)
S   1 dead on road Gargunnock 8th December (RAB) (sole records, Editor)

LONG-EARED OWL *Asio otus*
C   1 Alva 14th-17th October, flying over gorse by daylight (SFN)
SWP   nest with 2 young in old crow's nest Tyndrum 18th May (RAB). 1 Blaircreich (Inverlochlarig) 11th August (WRB)

SHORT-EARED OWL *Asio flammeus*
F   3 Kinneil 17th January (DCJ). 1 Skinflats 16th August (DMB)
C   1 Cambus 19th November and 30th December (CJH SFN)
SWP   1 Menteith Hills 21st May, 3 pairs Cromlix, 1 pair Glen Scione (Inverlochlarig) (WRB DT). 1 Sheriffmuir 2nd July (MVB).

SWIFT *Apus apus*
S   80 Bridge of Allan 21st July (DMB), last at colony 8th August (CJH). 1 Polmaise 4th May, 1 Airthrey on 3rd and 4 on 8th, 1 Buchlyvie on 9th; over Stirling 13 May to 11th August (DMB RAB MVB DT)

C   At Alva 13th May to 11th August (SFN)
SWP   4 pairs nesting on aqueduct in Loch Ard Forest — young heard calling 24th June (JC)

KINGFISHER *Alcedo atthis*
F   1 Grangemouth, River Avon (NS937798) 22nd February (JW)
C   At Cambus: 1 on 28th September and 1 by Forth on 19th November (CJH IW)
S   1 dead at Airthrey on 15th February, 2 on 10th March and 1 on 29th September (DMB SFN)
SWP   1 Ashfield 25th July (WRB)

WRYNECK *Jynx torquilla*
C   1 by River Devon at Alva 10th October, flushed out of hawthorns (SFN)

GREEN WOODPECKER *Picus viridis*
S   At Plean, Blairlodge and Abbey Craig wood in April, 4 young Airthrey on 15th July (MVB WRB SFN)
C   Fledged young seen in July and August at 2 sites Menstrie-Alva and 2 sites at Tillicoultry. 1 Vicar's Bridge 6th April (SFN)

GREAT SPOTTED WOODPECKER *Dendrocopus major*
C   Drumming in April at 2 sites by Devon at Dollar. 1 Linn Mill 13th April. Drumming Balquharn 5th May and adult with fledged young seen Alva 8th July (SFN)
S   2 drumming Plean 14th April. Male Airthrey 10th May (IW). Bridge of Allan 3rd and 19th November (WRB SFN). At birdtable Stirling from 24th October, 3 on 22nd December (IW)
SWP   2 Blairdrummond 17th April (WRB). Bred Trossachs and Loch Chon (JC)

SKYLARK *Alauda arvensis*
F   40 Kinneil 2nd January and 50 on 13th March (DCJ)
C   Flocks in stubble at Alva from 29th September, 37 on 23rd November (SFN)
SWP   Widespread, occasional song, Braeleny 13th March (CJH)

SAND MARTIN *Riparia riparia*
C   1st on River Devon at Alva 15th April, prospecting holes on 26th, 32 burrows, 4 pairs above Dollar (SFN)
S   1 Airthrey 13th April and 40 on 27th (MVB)
SWP   1 Lake of Menteith 13th April (DT). 4 Barbush 4th April and 40 on 15th (WRB), 620 occupied burrows on 20th June (DMB)

SWALLOW *Hirundo rustica*
C 1st Alva 11th April (SFN)
S Last Stirling on 9th October (DT). First Airthrey 12th April and last 24th October (DMB)
SWP 2 Lake of Menteith 13th April (DT), 3 Ashfield on 15th (WRB)

HOUSE MARTIN *Delichon urbica*
S 2 Airthrey 18th April, 5 on 21st; 2 on 18th October (DMB MVB)
C Last at Alva 19th September (SFN)
SWP 120 Dunblane 17th September (MVB)

TREE PIPIT *Anthus trivialis*
C Several on slopes above Alva June-July, fledged young seen 2nd August (SFN)
SWP 2 singing Tyndrum 20th April. Singing Menteith Hills 21st May. 2 pairs Drumore Wood in June (WRB DT). Widespread in Loch Ard Forest, present in 9 of 12 tetrads visited in NN40 (JC)

MEADOW PIPIT *Anthus pratensis*
S 15 Touch Hills 12th March (CJH)
SWP Flocks at Frandy 28th March included 2 with reddy-orange throats (SFN)

ROCK PIPIT *Anthus petrosus*
F 3 Kinneil 30th January and 1 on 15th October; 3 Blackness 6th November (CJH DCJ)

GREY WAGTAIL *Motacilla cinerea*
S 2 at Airthrey as early as 25th May (MVB)

PIED WAGTAIL *Motacilla alba*
F 50 Kinneil 13th March. 4 White Wagtails Kinneil 4th May and 1 Skinflats on 15th September (DCJ)
S At Airthrey roost: 170 on 2nd October; 70 on 22nd November, roosting at 16.00 in Kerria japonica in a sheltered delivery yard (MVB CJH). 200 Stirling 5th August, roost in on roof of Thistle Centre (SFN)

WAXWING *Bombycilla garrulax*
S 5 arrived Stirling 9th December, left after 5 min (IW). 1 Fallin 21st December (DCJ)
SWP 1 Doune Ponds 1st November and 1st December, 2 Bridge of Allan early December (WRB)

DIPPER *Cinclus cinclus*
C/SWP About 80 pairs in monitored area (all the River Devon and its

tributaries, most of the Allan Water and some of the Teith), similar to previous year. Eggs in some nests in early March — almost a month earlier than usual. Thus some young from lowland nests had fledged by mid-April, and probably many more pairs than usual raised second broods.

A female nestling from a nest on the Teith at Deanston (Doune) was caught on an autumn territory just below Castlehill Dam on the Devon (i. e. above Muckhart) — 30 km east. This is the first record of a move from Teith to Devon and the longest recorded dispersal distance to date (SFN — Univ. of Stirling study)

WREN *Troglodytes troglodytes*
SWP   Most widespread breeding species in Loch Ard Forest, present in 11 of 12 tetrads visited (JC)

ROBIN *Erithacus rubecula*
S   Regularly coming to scraps on a third storey windowledge in Bridge of Allan through autumn (CJH)

REDSTART *Phoenicurus phoenicurus*
SWP   6 pairs Drumore Wood (WRB). Trossachs: 39 nests fledged 175 young (HR)

WHINCHAT *Saxicola rubetra*
C   10 in 2 km of Burn of Sorrow (Dollar) 19th May. 8 in wheat at Alva 23rd July to 6th September (SFN)
SWP   1 Menteith Hills 21st May (DT)

WHEATEAR *Oenanthe oenanthe*
F   4 Kinneil 14th August (DCJ)
S   3 males Lower Earlsburn Reservoir 2nd April (DT)
SWP   Male Inverlochlarig (Balquhidder) 27th March (RAB). 1 Barbush 2nd April (WRB). 1 Glendevon 12th April (SFN). 2 Killin 7th April (A. S. Moore)

RING OUZEL *Turdus torquata*
C   1 at 75m in gorse above Alva 12th September (SFN)
SWP   1 Killin (Beinn nan Eachan NN575383) 7th April (A. S. Moore). 2 Kirkton Glen 17th April and 2 Beinn a Chroin, Balquhidder, 28th August (RAB IW). Not seen during Atlas work in upper Balquhidder NN41 (DM)

FIELDFARE *Turdus pilaris*
F   250 Blackness 6th November (CJH)
C   75 Dollar 2nd April. 6 Alva 16th October, 50 on 29th, left by early November when haws eaten (SFN). 120 Cambus 6th November (WRB)

S   100 SW Airthrey at 11.00 28th October (CJH), 80 on 13th December (MVB). 100 Cambuskenneth 31st October (IW)

SWP 40 Lecropt 23rd January, 250 Chalmerston 7th February, 150 Sheriffmuir 5th April, 40 Thornhill and 200 Ashfield 17th April, 1 Cambushinnie 15th May (MVB WRB DT).
250 Lecropt, 200 Thornhill and 300 Loch Laggan 22nd October; 250 Duncrook 20th November (DT)

REDWING *Turdus iliacus*
C   First Alva 10th October, 26 on 15th (SFN)
SWP 45 Lecropt 23rd January. Scarce in autumn, some on Carse of Stirling on 22nd October (DT)

GRASSHOPPER WARBLER *Locustella naevia*
F   1 Skinflats 4th May (DCJ)
C   1 singing in Juncus flush at Alva 30th June, 1 in gorse nearby 5th September (SFN)
S   1 singing Blairlogie 24th April (WRB)
SWP 2 singing in marshy thicket by River Larig, Balquhidder 15th May (DM). 1 Lecropt 15th June (WRB)

SEDGE WARBLER *Acrocephalus schoenobaenus*
C   2 singing Cambus (WRB). First Alva 2nd May; 9 singing in 800m (SFN)
S   1 Airthrey 5th May, Fallin on 13th (MVB DT)
SWP 3 pairs Ashfield railway, pair at Doune Ponds after several years absence (WRB)

LESSER WHITETHROAT *Sylvia curruca*
SWP 1 singing Laighhills Park, Dunblane, 25th April (WRB)

WHITETHROAT *Sylvia communis*
C   3 territories Alva, 2 on hillside, 1 by river (SFN)
S   1 Fallin 13th May (DT). Male Airthrey 27th May-8th June (MVB)

GARDEN WARBLER *Sylvia borin*
SWP 2 singing Lake of Menteith 6th May (RAB). 1 Loch Chon 18th May, confirmed breeding (JC)

BLACKCAP *Sylvia atricapilla*
F   Male Bo'ness 12th and 13th November, with House Sparrows (PDT). 1 Kinneil 10th May (DCJ)
S   Male Cornton 4th January, stayed 2 weeks frequenting an evergreen honeysuckle (RJF). Male Airthrey 25th April (MVB). Male Stirling 12th April and on 28th December (IW)

WOOD WARBLER *Phylloscopus sibilitrax*
S   1 Airthrey 7th May (DMB)

CHIFF CHAFF *Phylloscopus collybita*
S   3 singing Bridge of Allan 13th April, 2 Plean on 14th (WRB
         JC), 1 Airthrey 19th April, 1 territory (MVB)
C   1 Crook of Devon 15th April (DMB)
SWP   1 Lake of Menteith 1st April, Rednock Wood on 2nd, Dunblane
         on 6th (WRB MNB DT). 5 singing Loch Ard Forest (East end)
         3rd May (JC). Last at Doune Ponds 13th September (WRB)

WILLOW WARBLER *Phylloscopus trochilus*
C   First Alva 21st April (SFN)
S   3 singing Airthrey 13th April (MVB)
SWP   2 Barbush and Dunning 15th April, Blairdrummond and Lake
         of Menteith on 17th (WRB DMB DT). Present in 10 of 12 tetrads
         visited in Loch Ard Forest NN40 (JC). 16 in a tit flock Dunblane
         5th September (MVB)

SPOTTED FLYCATCHER *Muscicapa striata*
C   2 Alva 24th May (SFN)
S   1 Airthrey 27th May (MVB)

PIED FLYCATCHER *Ficedula hypoleuca*
SWP   Trossachs: 71 nests fledged 340 young (HR). 1 singing Loch
         Chon 18th May (JC)

LONG-TAILED TIT *Aegithalos caudatus*
SWP   21 Dunblane 2nd September (MVB)

RED-BACKED SHRIKE *Lanius excubitor*
SWP   Male near Lake of Menteith 3rd June, around a clump of
         Blackthorn and Hawthorn. Not seen subsequently (R. K.
         Pollard)

JAY *Garrulus glandarius*
F   1 Callendar Park 8th May (PDT)
C   1 Gartmorn Dam 19th November (PDT)
S   2 Plean 14th April (WRB)
SWP   Usual records in gardens in Callander (WRB)

MAGPIE *Pica pica*
S   14 Airthrey 14th March (DMB)
SWP   2 Tyndrum 6th November (RAB)

ROOK *Corvus frugilegus*
S   Roosting at Bridge of Allan: many (with Jackdaws) flying SE on

27th March at 19.40, 2hrs after sunset; 1500 S at 16.00 on 20th November (CJH).
Rookeries, 19th April: Bridge of Allan, 115 S (38 Kenilworth Rd), 69 N (34 in pines, probably overlooked previously). 33 Witches Craig (Blairlogie) (CJH)

RAVEN *Corvus corax*

Of 16 territories checked, 13 were occupied by pairs; 10 bred successfully with 5 pairs producing 19 young (PSA)

C   Scarce this year in Ochils, 1 on 26th May and 2 on 25th September (SFN). 2 North Third Reservoir 13th November (WRB)

S   3 Lower Earlsburn Reservoir 2nd April. 4 Loch Laggan 22nd October (DT)

SWP   2 Ashfield 12th January, 2 Braeleny 13th March, 2 Torrie Forest 9th September and 15th November (WRB CJH DT)

STARLING *Sturnus vulgaris*

C   Kincardine Bridge roost: 1000 on 20th February, 2000 on October 30th (CJH)

HOUSE SPARROW *Passer domesticus*

F   100 Skinflats 14th August (DCJ)

TREE SPARROW *Passer montanus*

F   30 Upper Kinneil 13th November (DCJ)
C   12 Cambus 20th January (WRB). 13 Alva 19th March (SFN)
S   50 in playing field Cornton 7th October (IW)
SWP   4 Lecropt 23rd January, 15 on 15th June and 100 on 18th November. 5 Arnprior 18th October (WRB RAB DT)

CHAFFINCH *Fringilla coelebs*

C   Largest flock at Alva only 60 on 23rd September (SFN)
SWP   Territories in 10 of 12 tetrads visited in Loch Ard Forest NN40 (JC). 500 Callendar 6th November (RAB)

BRAMBLING *Fringilla montifringilla*

SWP   1 Ashfield 2nd January and 5 Arnprior on 3rd (WRB DT). 2 Callendar 6th November and 1 Thornhill on 18th, all with Chaffinches (RAB)

GREENFINCH *Carduelis chloris*

S   75 Cambuskenneth 11th August (IW)

GOLDFINCH *Carduelis carduelis*

C   12 Alva on 5th and 23rd November; 20 Cambus 30th December (SFN)

SWP   15 Lake of Menteith 14th January (RAB)

SISKIN *Carduelis spinus*
F   25 Bo'ness 6th November (CJH)
C   40 Muckhart 18th September (DMB)
SWP   30 Dunblane 15th September, 20 Doune Ponds 1st November (MVB WRB)

LINNET *Carduelis cannabina*
F   150 Grangemouth 31st January (MVB), 40 Skinflats 6th April (DCJ)
C   25 Cambus 19th November (CJH)
S   20 Cambuskenneth 23rd May (IW)

TWITE *Carduelis flavirostris*
F   140 Grangemouth 17th January (DMB). 7 Kinneil 17th January and 13 on 30th; 7 on 10th December (DCJ)
C   Pair Upper Glendevon Reservoir 26th May (SFN)
SWP   Present Killin 7th April — Meall Garbh NN576382 (830m), Creag na Caillich NN562368 (A. S. Moore)

REDPOLL *Carduelis flammea*
C   Absent from usual breeding site at Upper Glendevon Reservoir (SFN)

CROSSBILL *Loxia curvirostra*
F   On 10th October 6 Barnsmuir (NS8570) and 2 Limerigg (NS8770) (RAB)
S   1 W at Bridge of Allan 25th August, 4 Darach Hill 18th November, 1 singing Carron Valley Forest 14th January, 4 on 26th December (DMB CJH DCJ). Max of 3 Airthrey 6th and 17th June and 15th July (MVB)
SWP   3 Achray Forest 24th January and 4 on 27th March; 6 Aberfoyle quarry 10th March (beak found on raptor kill), 5 Loch Ard Forest 18th May; 4 Menteith Hills 23rd June (WRB JC DT)

BULLFINCH *Pyrrhula pyrrhula*
SWP   Seen in summer in 9 of 12 tetrads visited in Loch Ard Forest (JC)

HAWFINCH *Coccothraustes coccothraustes*
SWP   2 Moray Park, Doune, 4th February, 1 reported in December (WRB)

SNOW BUNTING *Plectrophenax nivalis*
F   1 Kinneil 20th November (DT)
S   80 E Darrach Hill 18th November (CJH)

SWP   2 Glen Gaoithe 27th February (RAB)

YELLOWHAMMER *Emberiza citrinella*
C   20 in arable at Alva 16th October (SFN)

REED BUNTING *Emberiza schoeniclus*
F   30 Kinneil 2nd January and 40 on 17th (DCJ)
C   2 Pairs Cambus (WRB). 15 by Devon at Alva 23rd November (SFN)
SWP   2 Lecropt marsh 15th June, pair Doune Ponds (WRB). 12 Loch Arklet 12 April (IW)

CORN BUNTING *Miliaria calandra*
F   5 singing males Skinflats-Powfowlis 19th April (DCJ)
C   4 at Blackgrange (Cambus) 20th January (WRB)

The following species occur in the Region but no notes have been received that warrant publication for this year:

KESTREL *Falco tinnunculus*   GOLDCREST *Regulus regulus*
GREY PARTRIDGE *Perdix perdix*   COAL TIT *Parus ater*
PHEASANT *Phasianus colchicus*   BLUE TIT *Parus caeruleus*
TAWNY OWL *Strix aluco*   GREAT TIT *Parus major*
DUNNOCK *Prunella modularis*   TREECREEPER *Certhia familiaris*
BLACKBIRD *Turdus merula*   CARRION CROW *Corvus corone*
MISTLE THRUSH *Turdus viscivorus*

Editorial Note on Bird Reports

Previous reports for central Scotland or Forth Area were published in volumes 1 to 4 1974 to 1979 as *Stirling and Clackmannan Bird Report*, in volumes 5 to 10 1980 to 1986 as *Forth Area Bird Report (Clacks, Stirling, Southwest Perth)*, and for volume 11 1987 onwards as *Central Region Bird Report*.

Reports covering the whole of Scotland are published in *Scottish Bird Report*, and other Scottish areas local reports by recorders are published as follows (all available at the Scottish Ornithologists' Club, 21 Regent Terrace, Edinburgh, who organise the recording scheme), *Angus Wildlife Review; Argyll Bird Report; Ayrshire Bird Report; Borders Bird Report; Caithness Bird Report; Clyde Area Bird Report; Fair Isle Bird Report; Fife and Kinross Bird Report; Hebridean Naturalist; Lothian Bird Report; North-East Scotland Bird Report*; North Sea Bird Club's *Annual Report; Orkney Bird Report; Perthshire Bird Report; Shetland Bird Report*.

For other counties and regions, apply to their recorders. All recorders, and information on bird watching, recording, organisations, ringing, book reviews and feature articles, are given in *Birdwatchers' Yearbook and Diary* edited by John E. Pemberton, Buckingham Press (1989 edition 320pp £8.75).

BOOK REVIEW

FERRIES IN SCOTLAND. Marie Weir.
John Donald. 1988. 204pp. ppbk. ISBN 0 85976 235 1. £8.50.

From having her interest aroused by watching the Cramond ferry boat going to and fro across the Almond river near Edinburgh, Dr Weir has intensively researched primary and secondary sources to give us a rich mix of history and legend through 800 years.

She excludes ferries on lochs and canals, and those plying to and within Orkney and Shetland, and so disclaiming being comprehensive, leaves a challenge for someone to cover these which will be very hard to match.

She classes her ferries into seven chapters — the largest of over 40 pages being the river ferries; the Forth and Clyde Estuaries and the Islands have over 20 pages each; the Tay Estuary and the Northern Firths some 15 pages each. Prior to the 17th century there were at most 200 bridges in all Scotland, roads were mainly tracks formed by usage rather than by construction, and travelling any distance was an unenviable experience — to overcome the natural barriers of formidable rivers, hills and bogs. While there was a proliferation of bridge building in the 18th century real investment in bridges did not come till the early 1800s, so ferries were essential and numerous.

The wealth of information and anecdote, is absorbing — on ferries and ferry sites, travellers' experience, ferrymen and their way of life, and how these all coped with changing times.

The author's researches have culled a wide variety of sources — from primary documents and archives of government, agricultural, peace and road committees, town and burgh councils; through 18th and 19th century observations by travellers like Dorothy Wordsworth and James Boswell, Sir John Sinclair and writers in the Statistical Accounts, General Wade, Telford. . . .

In the chapter on the Forth Estuary ferries, and in relation to Queensferry, we read of a biblical like 'miracle' — when David I's cortege was going from Edinburgh Castle to Dunfermline in 1153 "the sea was so boisterous and agitated that they were afraid to venture upon it". However, as soon as the corpse was placed in the boat the storm abated and the opposite shore reached without difficulty. But, when the body got ashore the storm broke out again with renewed fury!

This is a well produced work one can highly commend, and Dr Weir gives 15 titles for further reading related to travel, from Burt's *Letters from a gentleman* . . . of 1745, to Fenton and Stell's *Loads and Roads in Scotland* . . . of 1984.

L. Corbett

DUTCH ELM DISEASE IN CENTRAL SCOTLAND

Ruth Neiland and J. W. Shepherd

INTRODUCTION

Dutch elm disease is one of the most destructive plant diseases known to Man. It infects most European and American species of elm, and has killed millions of trees throughout the Northern Hemisphere. In Britain alone 20 million elms, almost 90% of the population, have died (Gibbs 1979), the majority over the last two decades. This loss has had a devastating effect on the landscape of many areas, especially in southen England where elms were planted extensively in hedgerows. In Scotland too losses have been considerable, and Greensill (1977) identified Central Region as the most heavily infected part of the country.

Since 1977 many more elms have died, but there has also been considerable research into the disease and we now know a great deal more about control methods. Our aims in this paper are to—
(1) Discuss some of the recent findings as they relate to the ecology of Dutch elm disease in Scotland.
(2) Update information on the control of Dutch elm disease.
(3) Describe the progress of Dutch elm disease in central Scotland.

THE ECOLOGY OF DUTCH ELM DISEASE IN SCOTLAND

Dutch elm disease has only become a problem in Scotland since about 1970. In the 1920s and 30s when the first major known epidemic was sweeping across the south of England, very few cases were reported in Scotland, and most of these were confined to the Borders. The most northerly infection was in an avenue of elms between Inverkeithing and Cowdenbeath in Fife (Burdekin 1979). Also, mortality was the rare amongst infected trees. In the 1970s the disease became more widespread in Scotland, but the rate of infection was lower than in southern England (Greig and Gibbs 1983) although many trees died. In order to understand this pattern of disease development, it is necessary to study the ecology of Dutch elm disease with reference to the environmental factors influencing (a) the elm trees, (b) the pathogen (a fungus called *Ceratocystis ulmi*) and (c) the disease vector (beetles of the genus *Scolytus*).

(a) The Host

Elms are the only plants affected by the disease. There are several species and hybrids of elm in Britain, they vary in size, shape and appearance, but all share the characteristic oval, toothed leaves that grow singly on twigs and are usually asymmetric at the base (Figure 1). Infected

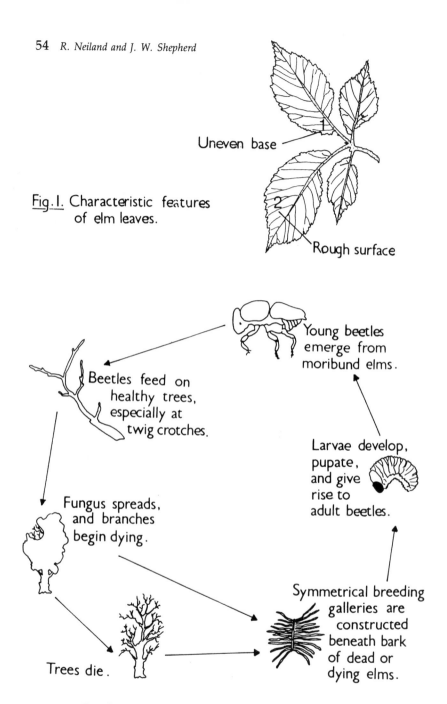

Uneven base

1

Fig.1. Characteristic features
of elm leaves.

2

Rough surface

Young beetles
emerge from
moribund elms.

Beetles feed on
healthy trees,
especially at
twig crotches.

Larvae develop,
pupate,
and give
rise to
adult beetles.

Fungus spreads,
and branches
begin dying.

Symmetrical breeding
galleries are
constructed
beneath bark
of dead or
dying elms.

Trees die.

Fig.2. Life cycle of Scolytus beetles.

trees show disease symptoms from mid-summer when the leaves become chlorotic (turn yellow) and the younger shoots tend to wilt. Initially this may only involve a few shoots which die back from the tip, but the symptoms usually spread and sometimes the tree may die within the first year, although some trees take several years to succumb.

Elms are thought to have grown in Britain for about two million years, although their numbers have fluctuated over that time. They disappeared completely during glaciations, but returned again with the milder climate of the interglacials (Moore 1985). The most recent invasion was about 9,000 years ago, after which their numbers dramatically increased, so that in southern England and Ireland the elm became the most common woodland tree. At the end of the Atlantic period however there was a rapid decline which did not affect other trees (Rackham 1980). Between 2900 and 3300 BC, about half the elm disappeared from Europe apparently because of Neolithic farming practices including the use of elm leaves as animal fodder, although disease may also have contributed. Certainly Man has had an important influence on the distribution of elms in more recent years. While woodland clearances have continued, elms were planted throughout Britain often outside their natural range in hedgerows, parklands and towns to fulfill various visual roles, and as a source of strong timber. They became a familiar component of the "typical" British lowland landscape, and were important as a habitat for birds and other wildlife.

The three most common elm species are the English Elm (*Ulmus procera*), the Wych Elm (*Ulmus glabra*), and the Smooth-Leaved or Wheatley Elm (*Ulmus carpinifolia*). All are liable to infections, but the English Elm is most prone to the disease (Brasier 1977), apparently because of its relative attractiveness to the disease vector, the elm bark beetle (*Scolytus* species). Experimental work by Webber and Kirby (1983) for example suggested that elms were selected for feeding by the beetles on the basis of their physical characteristics and chemical volatiles. English Elms are preferred because their rough bark is thought to stimulate feeding, as opposed to the smooth barks of the other elm species, and this initial preference is reinforced when feeding damage to the trees causes an increased release of host volatiles (such as ∞-cubebene, Byers et al 1981) which makes them even more attractive to the beetles. Further aggregation behaviour seems to be mediated by chemical pheromones produced by the beetles themselves when they feed on the host. A number of pheromones can be produced with different active components such as multistriatin and methylheptanols depending on the species, sex and maturity of the beetles involved. These pheromones can act in combination with chemicals released from the host to direct further beetle attack towards the less heavily colonised areas of the same trees, or to other trees (Grove 1983), thus assisting in the spread of the disease.

The predominant elm in Scotland is the Wych Elm, regarded by some as the only species native to Britain (Gibbs 1974). It is relatively unattractive to bark beetles compared to the English Elm, and this may partly explain the slower rate of disease transmission in Scotland. Perhaps more important however is the size and distribution of the elm population in this country. Grieg and Gibbs (1983) estimated that there were only seven million elms over 6m height in the whole of the north of Britain before the present epidemic. Even though their distribution was limited to river valleys and low land, as elms seldom grow on land over 250m above sea level, there was thus a tendency towards lower densities in Scotland than in the rest of Britain where there were more elms. Also, the genetically homogeneous populations common in southern England were generally not found. The Wych Elm differs from the other British species in that it usually reproduces by seeds rather then vegetatively. In England, many English and Smooth-Leaved Elms were planted in hedgerows, and when these reproduced by root suckers, the result was a row of trees all genetically identical, connected together via a linked root system, and thus more susceptible to infection by Dutch elm disease transmitted via the roots than individual Wych Elms, even when these grew in close proximity to each other.

(b) The Pathogen

The discovery of the cause of Dutch elm disease is attributed to Dutch scientists (hence the name) who pioneered research in the 1920s into an epidemic affecting trees in Europe and North America. They established that the disease was caused by a microscopic ascomycete fungus now called *Ceratocystis ulmi* (Buisman) C. Moreau (*Ophiostoma ulmi* (Buisman) Nannf.), which grows in the living tree mainly in a yeast-like form and is transported in the sap. The effects induced by this pathogen are complex and as yet not fully understood, but recent research has shown that it is the detrimental effect of the fungal metabolites on the physiology of the tree that leads to the wilt syndrome and necrosis characteristic of Dutch elm disease (Scheffer 1983). *C. ulmi* produces a number of cell-wall degrading enzymes and phytotoxic compounds, including cerato-ulmin and glycopeptides which act mainly on the parenchyma cells next to the water conducting xylem vessels of the tree. They release cell wall components which provide a source of nutrients for the fungus and promote its growth, and this, in conjunction with the deposition of cell debris in the vessel cavities, impedes water transport throughout the tree. Cell outgrowths called 'tyloses', which are produced by the host to try and confine the extent of the infection, also tend to block the vessels so that eventually the passage of water from the roots to the leaves is inhibited, and wilting and die-back occurs. The blocked vessels appear as an outer ring of darkly stained dots in a cross section of the wood.

The severity of symptoms is influenced by a number of factors such as genetic make-up, vigor, and age of the tree. For example, more resistant elm species have been shown to differ anatomically from more susceptible ones in the size and distribution of vessels, and to demonstrate faster tylose growth (Elgersma 1983), so that the spread of the pathogen is hampered. Environmental factors such as nutrient status, soil condition and temperature are also important (Gibbs 1978), as is the time of year that infection takes place (early infection frequently leads to early death), but the over-riding factor affecting the severity and distribution of the disease is the virulence of the pathogen.

It is now recognised that there are two strains of the *Ceratocystis ulmi* in Britain, and that one is more virulent than the other. Called the 'aggressive' and 'non-aggresive' strains, they were first identified in the late 1960s when, with the development of a new epidemic of Dutch elm disease in southern England, trees began to die at a faster rate than before (Gibbs and Brasier 1973). In the years since 1927 when the disease was first identified in Britain, most infected trees had recovered, and only 10-20% of the total elm population died. With the new strain however, affected trees often died within one growing season. Investigations by the Forestry Commission found that the aggressive strain had been introduced into the country on diseased logs of rock elm (*U. thomasii*) imported from Canada (Brasier and Gibbs 1973), but by the time the serious nature of the new epidemic was apparent, it was too well established for any effective control programme to be organised. The aggressive strain did not arrive in Scotland until the mid-1970s, but from then its effects were similar to those in the south, i.e. accelerated death rate amongst infected trees. The two strains can now be distinguished in culture, and one explanation for the virulent nature of the aggressive strain is its fast growth rate.

(c) The Vector

Dutch elm disease is mainly transmitted by elm bark bettles, three species of which are present in Britain, *Scolytus multistriatus* (Marsham), *S. laevis* (Chapuis) and *S. scolytus* (Fabr.), although only the latter occurs in Scotland. The beetles are specific to elm trees and their complex life cycle is linked with dead or dying elms, since they are unable to colonise or reproduce in healthy trees (Kirby et al 1982). Trees selected for breeding must already by weakened and so those infected with the disease provide an ideal host.

The life cycle of *Scolytus* beetles is shown in Figure 2. Once the beetles have emerged from moribund elms during the late spring / early summer, they spend some time feeding on the bark of healthy twigs, particularly the nutritious cambium layer. Although this behaviour was thought to be a prerequisite for sexual maturation, recent research suggests that such feeding is instead initiated by the need to obtain water and nutrients (Kirby and Fairhurst 1983). The beetles tend to bore preferentially into the twig axils or crotches, and in doing so they penetrate the xylem. If they have come from trees infected with the disease, they will pass fungal spores into the vascular system of the healthy tree. When the beetles have fed, they search for moribund trees in which to breed. These trees often become badly attacked because pheromones which induce aggregation are produced by the pioneer beetles. After mating the females lay their eggs in galleries tunnelled into the sapwood, and when these hatch, the larvae also feed by burrowing into the softwood. The symmetrical breeding galleries subsequently produced provide ideal sheltered sites for the production of fungal fruiting bodies, so that when, after pupating, the young beetles eventually leave the tree as adult insects, their bodies are covered with fungal spores. These emergence flights are often synchronised and the tree may appear to have been peppered with shot because of the large number of small round exit holes.

A number of factors are known to influence the behaviour of elm bark beetles and therefore to indirectly affect the transmission of the disease. For example, colonisation of host trees is sometimes inhibited by a saprophytic fungus *Phomopsis oblonga* (Webber 1981), which competes for space with the beetles in the breeding galleries and prevents development of larvae. Massive colonisation of elm bark by *Phomopsis* has mainly been observed in Wych Elm, and according to Webber (1981) it is more common in the north of Britain, which may have contributed to the initial lower infection rate in Scotland. Similarly, recent research identified *Pseudomonas* bacteria as being anatagonistic towards *Ceratocystis ulmi* in elms, and suggested that it could be used as a form of biological control (Scheffer 1983).

Beetle emergence and flight are also very much affected by weather conditions (Crowson 1976). They seem to be restricted to days when temperatures are between 15 and 31°C, with the optimum temperature being 21°C (Water 1981), and directional flight is inhibited when winds exceed 5m/s. Thus adverse weather conditions which provide sub-threshold flight temperatures or excessive winds prevent beetles from locating and colonising elms and may result in insects' death from dessication within three days. Since such adverse weather is more common in the north of Britain, the effect of climate on the dispersal of bark beetles seems to have been important in restricting the rate of spread of the disease in Scotland. Warm weather enhances the spread of the disease, since a mild spring and summer not only provide optimum flight temperatures, but also allow the emergence of a second brood of beetles within the same season. Thus, the effect of a series of warm summers in Scotland in the 1970s was to spread the beetles and the disease further north than previously (Greensill 1977), and ultimately make some form of control necessary if Scottish elms were to be conserved.

CONTROL OF DUTCH ELM DISEASE

Research carried out within the last ten years has not only increased our knowledge of the ecology of the disease, but has also had important implications for control policy.

The basis of control methods is **sanitation felling** by which infected elms are cut down and the bark destroyed to eliminate the breeding grounds for the beetles. This technique has been tried in many countries over the years, and has met with varying degrees of success, e.g. in the United States (Burdekin 1979); in Britain (Greig and Gibbs 1983); and in the Netherlands (Water 1983). It is now clear that for sanitation felling to be effective, all diseased elms within a region have to be removed immediately the disease is identified. This is virtually impossible to achieve in practice, but if the majority of infected elms are felled, the rate of spread of the disease can be slowed considerably. Certainly, the most successful sanitation programmes have been those where trees were inspected regularly and diseased elms were removed promptly (Greig and Gibbs 1983), and this was most easily achieved when the elm population was geographically isolated from sources of new infection. Sometimes it is possible to save trees showing only very slight symptoms by pruning out the diseased branches, and, where practicable, spread of the disease between adjacent trees via the roots can be halted by trenching to sever the root connections. Sanitation felling is expensive, e.g. the Dutch spent £1.5 million per annum (Spinks 1986), but the technique has proved cost effective in many areas since, in its absence, many more dead elms would have to be removed for safety and aesthetic reasons (Bliss 1981).

Sanitation felling can be supplemented by **tree trap techniques** which attempt to artificially manipulate the aggregation behaviour of the elm bark beetles. *Scolytus* species are naturally attracted to elms by chemical volatiles called 'pheromones' produced by beetles when they bore into elm bark. The active components of these pheromones have been identified as methylheptanols (Blight 1980), and it is now possible to formulate baits for beetle traps using natural or synthetically produced pheromone chemicals. Trap techniques are useful in the monitoring and surveillance of beetle populations, but can also be used to suppress their numbers as shown at New York State University (O'Callaghan and Fairhurst 1983). They prevented reproduction of *Scolytus multistriatus* beetles by attracting them to elms which had been killed with the arboricide, cacodylic acid. Their broods fail to develop in the treated areas, possibly because of the rapid decline in bark moisture levels. Unfortunately, tests have not been so promising with *Scolytus scolytus*, the species present in Scotland, because their flight behaviour is not so strongly mediated by pheromones, and so the main use of the technique in this country would be in the monitoring of beetle flights.

Insecticides can be used to control the beetle before it introduces the fungus into the tree. The insecticide DDT was used extensively for this, but was shown to have adverse effects on wildlife. Methoxychlor was substituted after DDT was banned, but since it is highly toxic to aquatic life, its widespread use is not recommended (Scott and Walker 1975).

In order to prevent infection by the fungus, individual trees can be injected with **fungicides**, the most commonly used being 'Lignasan' (carbenadzin hydrochloride). It is expensive because each tree has to be injected annually in order to maintain the correct dose throughout the canopy, and administering the high concentrations and volumes needed can be damaging to the tree. Also, it can only be considered as a preventative measure. Another common fungicide is 'Ceratotect' which is claimed to cure Dutch elm disease, provided it is injected into the tree in the early stages of infection. It has the advantage that it only needs to be injected every three years. Recently Dutch scientists have developed other fungicides including fenpropimorph, which can be easily administered by injecting into the roots or trunks of infected elms (New Scientist 1986). They inhibit the biosythesis of the fungus by preventing its conversion from the relatively dormant phase to the more dangerous mycelium phase. Research is continuing to develop slow release fungicide 'pills' which could be implanted into the trunks, and would be more cost effective than regular injections.

Forms of **biological control** which have been investigated include the effect of the fungus *Phomopsis oblonga* which prevents the development of eggs laid in elm bark (Webber 1981), and of the bacterium *Pseudomonas* spp. which act antagonistically towards *Ceratocystis ulmi* (Scheffer 1983). Also woodpeckers and other birds are natural predators of the bark beetle larvae, and it has been suggested that they could be used as a method of suppressing insect populations (Burdekin 1979). As yet it is not clear whether any of these methods could be successfully manipulated to control the disease.

Resistant species of elm have been developed over many years such as the 'Commelin' and 'Groenveld' elms planted extensively in the Netherlands in the 1960s, but most have proved to be susceptible to the aggressive strain of the disease (Heybroek 1988). The most recent strains have been developed from elms from Asia where *Ceratocystis ulmi* is thought to have originated, and these are the most promising. *Ulmus Sapporo* 'Autumn Gold' is now widely available in Britain and the United States, and although expensive, its cost is going down as it becomes commonly used. However, its appearance is very different to the indigenous British elms, and so it is not really a satisfactory substitute.

Many of these methods have been used in Central Region.

DUTCH ELM DISEASE IN CENTRAL REGION

Prior to the 1970s, the non-aggressive strain of the *Ceratocystis ulmi* fungus caused few problems in Central Region. Those elms that did become infected usually recovered. However, by the mid-1970s, the aggressive strain had arrived from southern England, probably transported on diseased timber. The disease was readily spread to the susceptible English elms in the area, especially those along the Hillfoots of the Ochils, by the elm bark beetles known to occur in the Region. (One of the reasons for the designation of Abbey Craig as a Site of Special Scientific Interest was because it was the most northerly recorded incidence of *Scolytus* spp. in Britain). Soon afterwards the disease spread amont the larger population of Wych elms, and many trees began to die.

In 1977 the Regional Council set up a team of three inspectors as a Manpower Services Commission Project. Their brief was to patrol the countryside, to identify outbreaks and to persuade landowners to fell and burn diseased trees. Nearly all landowners co-operated with this policy, and the spread of the disease was slowed considerably. A programme of amenity tree planting was also promoted in conjunction with derelict land clearances. But by 1980, the disease had become so widespread that sanitation was only possible near major centres of population. This change of policy was endorsed by the Forestry Commission, who co-ordinate the disease control work of Local Authorities.

Between 1980 and 1982 the disease was contained and urban areas had only limited outbreaks. However, the number of elms lost in the surrounding countryside rose steadily, and it became increasingly difficult to prevent infection and death. Stirling and Alloa were within range of the beetle population of the Hillfoots, and there were several deep glens where sanitation felling would have been impossible. Similarly, Falkirk was close to heavily diseased elm woodlands in the Lower Carron Valley. Replacement planting with common deciduous trees including oak, beech, birch and ash, was accelerated to offset these losses. By 1982, the only area where the disease could be slowed down by sanitation felling was Bo'ness, where the woodlands which dominate the hillside behind the town were relatively free of disease.

At this time, some of the control techniques described above were tested, one of the most successful being the first Scottish trial of the fungicide Ceratotect. There were two test sites. The first was a Weeping Elm (*Ulmus glabra*) in the grounds of the Regional Council offices at Viewforth. The treatment was successful for three years, as promised by the manufacturers, but in the fourth year, the tree contracted the disease and died. The other trees tested were along the River Forth, downstream of Stirling Bridge. Two of the large English elms injected are among the few healthy elms remaining in Stirling.

Figure 4 Dead Wych Elm.

Figure 3 Local elm tree beginning to succumb to Dutch elm disease and showing the characteristic yellowing of leaves in summer (arrowed).

Figure 5 Mature elms at Riverside, downstream of Stirling Bridge. They were injected with the fungicide 'Ceratocect' in 1982 and remain healthy in 1988.

Figure 6 Dead elm at Pitt Terrace, St Ninian's Road, Stirling.

In 1983, the outbreaks in Bo'ness became more serious, possibly because the disease was increasing in the Avon Valley, in Lothian Region, and across the River Forth in Fife. Replacement tree planting however, did continue and is still carried out today, and an advice service for landowners has also been maintained by the Regional Council Planning Department. Landowners are now advised to carry out felling on the grounds of safety rather than disease control, and injections are only recommended if the tree is considered important enough to warrant a continuing commitment to expenditure. The most important advice is to carry out replacement planting using a mixture of deciduous or broadleafed trees.

In 1987, just such a replacement tree planting campaign was mounted by Bridge of Allan Community Council. It was intended to counter the losses of hundreds of diseased trees from the woods around the village. In 1985-86 Stirling District Council's arborist and his team had felled 110 large elms over 15m, 162 medium sized trees, and 126 small trees under 9m in the woods around Bridge of Allan owned by that Council. In 1987-88 they felled 225 trees in Mine Woods, 50 in Westerton Wood, 135 on Abbey Craig, 172 in the Allan Bank Wood and 23 in the Allan Vale Road area. The tree planting campaign, conducted with the help of school children, raised over £1,000 from the local community, and the Community Council, arborist and rangers were subsequently able to plant several hundred young replacement trees in Mine Woods and nearby areas.

CONCLUSION

Dutch elm disease has continued to infect and kill trees in the Central Region of Scotland over the last ten years, so that now few healthy mature elms remain. Unfortunately, much of the recent research into the ecology and control of the disease has come too late to save trees in this Region, although the programme of sanitation felling did achieve the objective of slowing down the spread of the disease, and allowed time for some replacement planting to take place. We have learnt that sanitation can only succeed in containing the disease where the area involved is isolated from new infection, and monitoring is vigorously pursued. In Scotland, the only 'defensible area' where sanitation felling continues are in Edinburgh, Dundee, and parts of Glasgow.

In Central Region the disease is now considered to have run its course, and the number of cases of infection is decreasing as there are so few mature elms left. The number of elm bark beetles has also declined due to lack of hosts. There is some evidence of natural regeneration of elms from the stumps and roots of diseased trees, some of which have produced vigorous suckers, and a proportion of these may survive, since the elm bark beetle cannot breed in trees of narrow girth. But we cannot rely on natural regeneration to replace those trees which have died, especially since there are now few places where suckers will be allowed to grow because of grass cutting practices, stock grazing, ploughing, and heribicide use. The only effective course of action to restore the losses is to continue with an extensive programme of tree planting with a mixture of native tree species (five as a minimum) so that any future diseases will not result in such a severe loss as caused by Dutch elm disease.

References

BLIGHT M. M., KING, C. J., WADHAMS, L. J. and WENHAM, M. J., 1980. Studies on chemically mediated behaviour in the large elm beetle *Scolytus scolytus* (F.) (*Coleoptera: Scolytidae*); Field Trials, 1979. Forestry Commission Research and Development Paper 129. 34pp.

BLISS, M. 1981. The basis and management of Dutch elm disease control. *Tree News – Tree Council Newsletter*.

BRASIER, C. M. 1977. Inheritance of pathogenicity and cultural characters in *Ceratocystis ulmi*: hybridization of protoperithecial and non-aggressive strains. *Transactions of the British Mycological Society* 68, 45-52.

BURDEKIN, D. 1979. Beetle and fungus — the unholy alliance. Chapter 4 in After the Elm. Edited by B. Clouston and K. Stansfield. Holmes and Meier.

BURDEKIN, D. Editor, 1983. Research on Dutch elm disease in Europe. Forestry Commission Bulletin No. 60. Her Majesty's Stationery Office, London. 134pp. Includes — Elgersma, D. M. Host-parasite interactions in Dutch elm disease. pp 78-81; Greig, B. J. W. and Gibbs, J. N. Control of Dutch elm disease in Britain. pp 10-16; Grove, J. F. Biochemical investigations related to Dutch elm disease carried out at the Agricultural Research Council Unit of Invertebrate Chemistry and Physiology, University of Sussex. pp 59-66; Heybroek, H. M. Resistant elms for Europe. pp 108-113; Kirby, S. G. and Fairhurst, C. P. The ecology of elm bark beetles in northern England. pp 29-39; O'Callaghan, D. P. and Fairhurst, C. P. Evaluation of the trap tree technique for the control of Dutch elm disease in northwest England. pp 23-28; Scheffer, R. F. Biological control of Dutch elm disease by Pseudomonas species, pp 75-78; Water, J. K. Dutch elm disease control in the Netherlands, pp 17-18; Webber, J. F. and Kirby, S. G. Host-feeding preference of Scolytus scolytus. pp 47-49.

BYERS, J. A., SVIHRA, P. and KOEHLER, C. S. 1980. Attraction of elm bark beetles to cut limbs on elm. *Journal of Arboriculture* 6, 245-246.

CROWSON, R. A. 1976. Elm bark beetles and elm disease in Scotland. *Glasgow Naturalist* 19, 317-319.

GIBBS, J. N. 1978. Intercontinental epidemiology of Dutch elm disease. *Annual Review of Phytopathology* 16, 287-307.

GIBBS, J. N. 1979. Dutch elm disease: survey 1978. Forestry Commission Report on Forest Research, 1979. pp 30-31. Her Majesty's Stationery Office, London.

GREENSILL, E. N. 1977. Dutch elm disease in Central Scotland. *Forth Naturalist and Historian*. 2, 71-78.

MOORE, P. The death of the elm. *New Scientist*, 25th June, 1985.

NEW SCIENTIST. Dutch find cure for elm disease. 7th August, 1986.

OSBOURNE, L. and KREBS, J. Replanting after Dutch elm disease. *New Scientist,* 23rd April, 1981, pp 212-215.

RACKHAM, O. 1980. Ancient woodland: its history, vegetation and uses in England. Edward Arnold.

RITCHIE, C. 1985. Phomopsis oblonga — a microgeographical survey. Unpublished B.Sc. honours thesis, University of Strathclyde.

SCOTT, T. M. and WALKER, C. 1975. Experiments with insecticides for the control of Dutch elm disease. Forestry Commission Record 105. Her Majesty's Stationery Office, London.

SPINKS, P. Dutch bark up the right tree. *The Guardian,* 22nd August, 1986.

WEBBER, J. F. 1981. A natural biological control of Dutch elm disease. *Nature.* 292, 449-451.

Authors/Reviewers Addresses

Angus, David, 122 Henderson Street, Bridge of Allan.

Ballantyne, G. H., Branksome, 193 Nicol Street, Kirkcaldy.

Corbett, L., Forth Naturalist and Historian, University of Stirling.

Elliott, B. J., Department of Education, University of Stirling.

Harrison, S. J., Department of Environmental Science, University of Stirling.

Henty, C. J., Department of Psychology, University of Stirling.

Muirhead, Andrew, Stirling District Libraries, Springkerse Estate, Stirling.

Neiland, Ruth, Department of Plant and Soil Science, University of Aberdeen.

Shaw, John, Royal Museum of Scotland, Queen Street, Edinburgh.

Shepherd, J. W., Planning Department, Central Regional Council, Viewforth, Stirling.

FLOWERS OF WEST FIFE: A SELECT ANNOTATED LIST

G. H. Ballantyne

At the end of the 18th century and during the first half of the 19th, it became evident to those botanists making their way over the Forth from Edinburgh that Fife was a rich county well worth exploring. In particular the immediate hinterland around Queensferry (the Ferry Hills) soon proved profitable, as did other favoured spots a little further afield. Thus West Fife soon built up a reputation as being an area that **had** to be visited, and to a degree this situation continued into this century. Alas, the visitors plundered as they searched, to our detriment today.

The earliest explorers concentrated on the Ferry Hills, with John Hope being credited with the first records in the 1760s, soon followed by John Mackay, George Don, and others. After the turn of the century the travellers began to go further and place names began to appear such as Limekilns, Charlestown and Culross to the west; St Davids, Donibristle and Aberdour to the east; and Dunfermline, the Saline Hills and the Black Devon to the north. Among Edinburgh botanists now coming over the ferry were Robert Maughan, Robert Greville and Robert Graham; while making local explorations, and adding a great deal to the knowledge of the flora, were the Rev. Alexander Robertson of Inverkeithing and Dr Andrew Dewar of Dunfermline.

Then J. H. Balfour was appointed Professor of Botany at Edinburgh in 1845 and he soon began a programme of early summer excursions with his students all over Scotland which was to last over 30 years. Being so close at hand, Fife was a favourite stopping off point and the parties paid several visits to West Fife. Thus the process of discovery went on, and this was continued by the two William Evans, father and son, at the end of the 19th and beginning of the 20th centuries. Another, who did much for our knowledge of aquatic plants, was George West who surveyed most lochs and reservoirs in 1905 (West 1910). Local interest was now low, especially as William Young of Kirkcaldy, who went on to compile the *List of the flowering plants . . . of Fife & Kinross* (1936), did little exploratory work in his native county, and with the opening of the Forth Bridge, from 1890 botanists were by-passing Fife on their way north.

Thus, apart from the continuing attraction of the Ferry Hills for a few, very little work was done between 1920 and 1970, when the present writer cast his net outwith his native Kirkcaldy district. Following the appointment of a full-time Assistant Regional Officer in Fife by the Nature Conservancy Council (NCC) in 1979, further exploration was carried out by Simon Leach and Nick Stewart, bringing to light just what had been lost, although there were some gains. Mention too may be made of Mr J. Carlyle of South Queensferry, who kept up the tradition of visiting the Ferry Hills in the 1950/60s.

Being a peninsula with a long coast line, Fife has long depended on the sea for its trade. This was especially the case in the 19th century when the small ports on the south coast were very busy, particularly in the export of coal. This meant that the incoming ships arrived in ballast, i.e. often loaded with earth and stones to weigh down the vessel. This ballast was dumped on arrival at the nearest convenient point and it did not take botanists long to realise that here was a source of unusual plants (Ballantyne 1971). Thus some places became renowned for alien species and were frequently visited, especially St Davids, just east of Inverkeithing. Resultant finds were not always looked upon favourably, however; in 1835, Graham commented "I should be afraid to consider **any** plant wild near that infected district" (author's emphasis). Most flowers did not last for more than a season or two but a few persisted and account for some comparatively unexpected occurrences today.

Another source of non-native plants is garden escapes or cast-outs, some of which have become naturalised, but it is only in more recent times that much attention has been paid to them. Many may now be fairly counted as part of the county's flora and indeed some woodlands would be almost featureless were it not for their naturalised spring flowers. A number have long been around but others are making their mark as they begin to spread, and this is also the case with some other species, accidentally introduced, and in a few instances now reaching weed status, e. g. *Epilobium ciliatum*.

Since the time of those early visits two centuries ago the countryside has in many places been altered beyond recognition, particularly since about 1900. Hope, Don and the like would scarcely know Queensferry and its surroundings — although the village itself is still relatively small, the two bridges dominate the area while to the west sprawls the Rosyth dockyard and to the east Inverkeithing and Dalgety Bay litter the landscape. And the same applies elsewhere, whether it be the past despoliation associated with the development of coal mining or the present utilisation of land for housing, industry, roads, etc. Perhaps the biggest current threats are improvements and changes in agricultural methods, and the new-found technology capable of altering almost every piece of countryside virtually overnight. No longer is **any** corner sacrosanct.

However, there are still a few spots where one can forget about 'progress', and become lost in appreciation of either individual plants or carpets of wild flowers, whether they be common or rare. One such place is the valley of the Black Devon river, especially behind the Saline Hills where it flows through Lethan's Den, in particular the stretch known as Swallowcraig Den. Despite recent attempts to 'improve' the latter, is is still "a little wild ravine, thickly and beautifully wooded and enlivened by a very romantic waterfall", as picturesquely described by the Rev. Hugh Macmillan in 1857. Here are no fewer than 16 species of sedge and a variety of flowers rare in Fife, as well as familiar plants — a total of 200 was recorded in 1978. Other rewarding retreats include Otterston Loch near Aberdour and the Black Loch near Dunduff, north of Dunfermline (the Black Loch in the Cleish Hills is mostly within Kinross-shire); Tipperton Moss west of Loch Glow and Dun Moss (what is left of it) west of Saline; and the coast at North Queensferry, at Aberdour and in the vicinity of Culross. There are still too odd hectares of old woodland that can reveal unexpected finds.

The area embraced, West Fife, corresponds to the present District of Dunfermline. It is unfortunate that for botanical purposes, quite a portion is outwith what is called vice-county 85. This is due to the fact that the botanical boundaries are based on the political boundaries as they were in the 1870s; these were altered in 1891, so that the parishes of Tulliallan and Culross, formerly in Perthshire, were transferred to Fife. This means that, botanically speaking, the SW part of the District is actually in West Perth (or VC87) and this should be borne in mind when these localities are mentioned. To the north lies Kinross-shire (Ballantyne 1977/85); to the west, Clackmannanshire; and to the east, Kirkcaldy District (Ballantyne 1970; 1982).

The list of species which follows is a subjective choice. It largely comprises those plants which the author considers to be worthy of mention, be it owing to rarity or extinction, attraction or idiosyncracy. The frequency and habitat details are based on observations made during the period 1967-86; visits were paid in most of these 20 years, in some frequently, in others a mere handful. Older records are taken from a variety of literature and herbarium sources, and in most instances an attempt was made to refind the plants. It should be noted that in the list, no effort has been made to include every record from a particular site — some are merely duplicates and others are often from about the same date. First records are usually given, and last ones where a species has not been seen recently. Occasionally, herbarium specimens have a different date from a published source, in which case the earlier is mentioned. Inevitably, some species listed as being extinct will be refound; in other cases, such is the speed of development that a few will disappear very soon. It is stressed that the selection is a personal one and no apology is made for including comparatively lengthy details of one or two obscure groups, e. g. brambles and willows. Some 340 species are mentioned out of a total of about 1150 recorded for the District, past and present. The latter figure is swollen by around 250 casual and impermanent species, about three-fifths of these being ballast introductions.

Although most of the observational work has been done by the author, significant contributions were made by Simon Leach, Nick Stewart and Helen Stace when they were employed by the NCC in the first half of the 1980s. The names of some other recorders are mentioned below and as appropriate in the text. Thanks to all, to Lindsay Corbett for his editorial encouragement, and to Mary Benstead for the map.

The nomenclature of the list follows Clapham, Tutin and Warburg, *Excursion Flora of the British Isles*, 3rd edition, 1981, names for *Rubus*, as E. S. Edees and A. Newton, *Brambles of the British Isles*, 1988.

Abbreviations used in the list in the form (. . .)—

(a) Herbaria: BM = British Museum; Kew = Kew Gardens; RBG = Royal Botanic Garden; StA = St Andrews University.

(b) Short forms for some of the references: B and S = Balfour and Sadler; Edinburgh = *Edinburgh Field Naturalists Society Transactions*; Glasgow = *Glasgow Natural History Society Proceedings*; NSA = New Statistical Account; BSE = *Botanical Society of Edinburgh Transactions*.

(c) Names given with initials are of modern recorders, not references of the paper: G. H. Ballantyne; B. J. Coppins; R. W. M. Corner; J. Crichton; A. C. Jermy; J. Kinloch; S. J. Leach; A. Mason; E. F. B. Spragge; H. E. Stace; N. F. Stewart; O. M. Stewart; I. M. Strachan; P. Taylor.

(d) The arrow → = and onwards to the present.

LIST OF SPECIES

Lycopodium clavatum (Stagshorn Clubmoss): According to one traveller in 1857 (Macmillan) both this and the next were 'abundant' on the Saline Hills, but not so now for many years. It must have occurred elsewhere but the only other record is from Cullalo in 1897 (Evans). Recent sightings were on various pit bings in the Kelty area in 1967 (R. W. M. Corner), but these have now been cleared away.

Huperzia selago (Fir Clubmoss): Seen on the Saline Hills in 1857 (see last entry), in the 1880s (Balfour), and near Cullalo in 1897 (Evans). Also on Moss Morran in 1870 (BM) and at Lethan's Den in 1919 (Templeman), but no recent records.

Isoetes lacustris (Quillwort): Found in 1975 in Kinross-shire in Lochs Dow and Lurg in the Cleish Hills, and discovered in nearby Loch Glow in 1984, where it had not been a year or two previously, the first Fife record.

Equisetum hyemale (Dutch Rush): There is one old record, from the banks of the Black Devon near Hillside, about the mid-19th century (RBG).

E. pratense (Shady Horsetail): The discovery of this uncommon plant at Lethan's Den in 1829 (StA) lead to the site being visited frequently for collecting — "it is so rare that all my friends have been supplied by me" (!!!) (Dewar corr. 1844). The last record was 1857 (Macmillan); not seen in recent years but conceivably might be refound.

E. x litorale: This hybrid between *E. arvense* and *fluviatile* was found in waste ground near Peppermill Dam in 1982.

Botrychium lunaria (Moonwort): Formerly widespread but now rare; as it is both easily overlooked and sporadic, it may still occur in some of its old localities. These include Lethan's Glen 1835 (Robertson) — 1858 (RBG); near Torryburn 1852-62 (RBG); Aberdour 1854-69 (Balfour); Knock Hill 1848-52 (Balfour); and Moss Morran 1869 (BM). Recently, seen only at the Ferry Hills in 1954/69.

Ophioglossum vulgatum (Adder's Tongue): There are quite a number of old records but only two recent sightings, in the Lethans area 1971 (J. Kinloch) and near Redcraigs cross-roads 1981 (S. J. Leach). Previous places where the plant could still occur, include the Torry area 1850s (Balfour); Aberdour 1854-71 (Balfour); and Saline area 1903 (Evans).

Osmunda regalis (Royal Fern): In the 1830s this species was reported to occur "in vast abundance" near Culross (Dewar corr.) There seems to have been two sites, near Blair Castle and near Sands Farm, Kincardine; by 1880 "from the rapacity of dealers and others, it has now disappeared" (Buchanan). It does grow, however, as an ornamental in Tulliallan Police College grounds, and near Torry House.

Matteucia struthiopteris (Ostrich Fern): Of the several species introduced during the Victorian fern craze this seems to be the only one which has survived, as at Fordell, Broomhall, Aberdour Den, and Bowershall (north of Dunfermline), all 1980→.

Cryptogramma crispa (Parsley Fern): This used to grow on the Saline Hills, from 1832 (RBG) to 1857 (Macmillan), when it was stated that it occurred "in immense profusion". Sadly it probably succumbed to a combination of over-collecting, quarrying and pollution years ago. There is no other West Fife record.

Phegopteris connectilis (Beech Fern): Becoming rare in Fife, the only Dunfermline District site being upper Lethan's Den, where it has been known since 1835 (Robertson).

Asplenium x alternifolium (Alternate-leaved Spleenwort): Discovered by Dewar in 1835 on Craigluscar Hill "in small quantity". Predictably this rarity was too much of an attraction for fern collectors, and it had gone within twenty years (Dewar corr.,*Phytologist*).

A. marinum (Sea Spleenwort): East of the Forth bridges, this maritime plant may still be found on rocks in the St Davids/Donibristle area where it has been known since 1838 (StA); but it has not been seen recently at North Queensferry (1809 Maughan) nor in the Limekilns district (1835 Robertson/1902 Evans).

Cystopteris fragilis (Bladder Fern): Very local, occasionally originally planted. Still by the Black Devon at Balgonar, maybe the 1837 RBG record; on the ruin of old Tulliallan Castle; and on Benarty, both 1980.

Dryopteris x deweveri: This hybrid buckler fern between *carthusiana* and *dilitata* was collected by Syme in 1876 from Humbie Wood, Aberdour. More recently found in 1983 on the southern part of Moss Morran,

Cowdenbeath; and by Moor Loch, Tulliallan (N. F. Stewart; A. C. Jermy).

Gymnocarpium dryopteris (Oak Fern): Occasional on rocky dens and dykes. Robertson listed it from Lethan's Den about 1835, and in 1857 Macmillan noted it by the roadside near Powmill, both localities still being extant. Also near Redcraigs cross-roads and near Balmule Farm, both north of Dunfermline, 1980→.

Pilularia globulifera (Pillwort): Known from the Tulliallan area before 1898 (White) and on Culross Moor, 1919 (Templeman), probably the same station. Refound in 1980 at Moor Loch by P. Taylor in some quantity and again in 1982 by N. F. Stewart, when only a few plants were present. The decline may have been due to lack of fluctuation in the water level; it is to be hoped that this nationally rare and diminishing species does not disappear from this, its sole Fife site (although in VC87).

Thalictrum minus (Meadow Rue): First listed as early as 1768 (Hope) from Carlin Nose, North Queensferry, this taxon has caused confusion ever since! The early botanists thought it was *T. flavum* but others considered it to be *T. majus*. In fact it is what is now named *T. minus* ssp. *majus*, and it still grows there, its only Fife locality. Ssp. *minus* has been known from Aberdour since 1820 (Boswell) and near Donibristle since 1849 (Balfour); formerly between Culross and Kincardine (1898 White).

T. majus: See last entry.

Trollius europaeus (Globe Flower): Rare, being known certainly only from Lethan's Den, which may well be Robertson's "north of Dunfermline" record of 1835 and Macmillan's 1857 "Hillside" station. Balfour also mentioned it from near Knock Farm in the 1850s "in large quantity"; this is not far from the Den.

Ranunculus auricomus (Goldilocks): This rather rare buttercup was noted about 1835 by Robertson in three localities — Woodmill, Fordell and Lethan's Glen. It is still definitely in the last, possibly at Fordell, but unlikely at Woodmill (Dunfermline). Balfour's 1850/60s records are almost certainly Aberdour Den where it still flourishes.

R. lingua (Greater Spearwort): Known from Otterston Loch since 1820 (Boswell); and at Loch Roy, Torrie House since before 1972. In Scotland this species may often be introduced, the latter site seemingly coming into this category.

R. circinatus (Water Crowfoot): Fife is fortunate in having a few sites for this Scottish rarity; in Dunfermline District it was found in Otterston Loch in 1863 (B and S) and 1905 (West) but has not been seen since. However, it is present in Lochore Meadows outflow.

R. baudotti (Brackish Water Crowfoot): In 1910, when discussing the abundance of *Ceratophyllum demersum* in Otterston Loch, G. West stated "I have noticed that *Ranunculus baudotii*, which was abundant at the east side of the loch in 1903, had in 1908 become almost extinct by the extension of the *Ceratophyllum*" (p163). As there is no other record, presumably the plant did disappear about then.

Berberis vulgaris (Barberry): One of the few Fife stations for this, albeit planted, are some hedges west of Aberdour, especially near Otterston, where it has been noted at regular intervals since 1855 (Balfour).

Nymphaea alba (White Water-Lily): Along with the next, still on the Black Loch, Dunduff, where it was described as "abundant" in 1835 (Robertson); and both on a pool in the Rescobie Hills, 1981→. As there has not been a 'Donibristle Loch' for some time, neither may be seen there! (1839 StA).

Nuphar lutea (Yellow Water-Lily): See last species; also at the west end of Loch Gelly, 1820 (Boswell)→; and on Loch Fitty, 1835 (Robertson)→.

Ceratophyllum demersum (Hornwort): Known since the 1890/1900s from Otterston Loch (RBG; Evans/West). In 1910, the last commented "it grows there in such extraordinary abundance that in many places a boat can only be rowed through it with difficulty" (p80 — see also *Ranunculus baudotii*). Sixty years later it was still present in much smaller quantity; but **not** seen in the 1980s.

Glaucium flavum (Yellow Horned Poppy): This attractive plant of the coast used to grace the Charlestown area between 1777 (Lightfoot) and 1855 (RBG); and North Queensferry from 1794 (RBG) to 1838 (StA). Alas it became extinct soon afterwards due probably to over-collecting and/or storms.

Corydalis claviculata (Climbing Corydalis): Formerly frequent, but nowadays occurring only in small quantity, as in Cullalo Reservoir area, 1820 (Boswell) and 1982 (N. F. Stewart); at Tulliallan, 1854 (Balfour) and 1988 (a lot); Roughcleugh Glen, 1981; Craigluscar, 1971 (E. F. B. Spragge); and Keirs Dam, Tulliallan Forest, 1985 (N. F. Stewart).

Diplotaxis tenuifolia (Wall Rocket): Plants introduced with ships' ballast occasionally establish themselves, as is the case with this species; recorded in 1821 at St Davids (Hooker), mentioned many times since, and still flourishing there. Also still at Charlestown (1886 Reid) but not at Inverkeithing, 1836 (Robertson) to 1890 (Glasgow).

D. muralis (Stinkweed): As with the last species, this was also a ballast alien, but only an odd plant is seen now, seldom persisting for long.

Cardaria draba (Hoary Cress): This alien from the Mediterranean is gradually spreading in Fife, and in Dunfermline District has established itself west of Aberdour; in Inverkeithing (by breaker's yard); and in the old station area near Kelty, all first seen about 1970.

Cochlearia danica (Early Scurvy-Grass): This dainty coastal flower was noted "by dyke at east landing", North Queensferry in 1801 (Mackay), and happily may still be observed there. However, not seen at Charlestown (1886 Reid) nor Culross (pre-1890 White); but growing on Horse Craig, near Crombie in 1981.

Bunias orientalis (Warty Cabbage): Thoroughly established on the west side of Inverkeithing Station, from before 1960→; also here and there as a non-persisting casual.

Arabis hirsuta (Hairy Rockcress): Rather uncommon, mostly coastal; still at the Ferry Hills where Robertson found it about 1835; near

Aberdour (i.e. Hawkcraig), 1939 (StA)→; and Charles Hill, 1980 (S. J. Leach). Also inland at Lethan's Den area, 1971→.

Viola odorata (Sweet Violet): An escape that naturalises fairly easily, but does not seem to have been seen for over a century. Old records include Inverkeithing, 1835 (Robertson) to 1885 (RBG).

V. hirta (Hairy Violet): Admired for nearly two centuries on the Ferry Hills, where MacRitchie first saw it in 1795, and still there is 1986. Also extant at Aberdour, where Balfour collected it in the 1860s. May still occur near Limekilns (1835 Robertson) and about Donibristle (1853-72 Balfour).

V. canina (Dog Violet): The true dog violet is rare in Fife and has almost certainly been over-recorded in the past — the very common *V. riviniana* is rather variable and the two can be confused. There are no recent definite sightings from West Fife, but it may remain in its two old haunts viz. the Aberdour area (1860s Balfour; RBG) and Ferry Hills (1856-72 Balfour).

V. tricolor (Heartsease): The true Heartsease is seldom seen, most records being variants of *V. arvensis* (Field Pansy). The sole modern record is from the Lethan's Den area in 1971.

V. lutea (Mountain Pansy): Fortunately, this pretty pansy is frequent, both in hilly regions e.g. Saline Hills, 1850s (Balfour) and 1971, and at low levels e.g. Pilkham Hills (Moss Morran), 1883 (RBG) and 1983.

Silene nutans (Nottingham Catchfly): Mentioned as occurring on rocks at the Ferry Hills between 1801 (Mackay) and 1826 (RBG), and perhaps later. In 1859 it was stated that it had not been found for the last twenty years (Chalmers), and there is no later record.

Dianthus deltoides (Maiden Pink): The only record is form Torryhill, north of Aberdour, in 1905 (StA) and 1919 (Templeman). Not seen recently, but could still grow there, and just possibly elsewhere.

Saponaria officinalis (Soapwort): Mentioned at regular intervals since 1835 (Robertson) at Inverkeithing and still to be glimpsed from trains on banks west of the tunnel; perhaps originally introduced with ballast, as it was near Charlestown in the 1850s (RBG).

Cerastium arvense (Field Mouse-ear): Although common in NE Fife, this plant decreases markedly westwards and in fact has been seen only once in the west, at Shire's Mill in 1973. It seems certain to grow in a few other spots.

Stellaria nemorum (Wood Stitchwort): This attractive plant favours wooded stream-sides and is common by the Black Devon, e.g. in Lethan's Den, near Little Saline and at Piperpool. Also by the Bluther Burn here and there; but not seen near Rosyth Castle (1849 RBG), its only previously recorded site.

Sagina subulata (Heath Pearlwort): Discovered on the Ferry Hills in 1801 (Mackay) and 35 years later considered to occur there in ''many places'' (Robertson) and present in 1870 (RBG). However, although not seen for over a century, it may still be there; but unlikely at Donibristle (1850s Balfour). Today, to be found on both the Cullalo and south

Cleish Hills, on the latter at Craigencat.

S. nodosa (Knotted Pearlwort): Present in other parts of Fife and Kinross, but not seen in recent years in the west. The two old records are North Queensferry (1857 RBG) and Cullalo (1905 West).

Arenaria balearica (Mossy Pearlwort): Thoroughly naturalised on tree roots in the Gellet Rock area of Broomhall Estate, 1971→.

Scleranthus annuus (Knawel): Uncommon on or by dry, gravelly tracks or banks; known on the Ferry Hills since 1824 (Woodforde)→. Also on the Cullalo Hills and in the Lochornie area, and perhaps elsewhere.

Chenopodium bonus-henricus (Good King Henry): There are a scattering of records of this old farmyard plant, including the Limekilns area (1848/1906, RBG), but no recent sightings. It ought to be present somewhere!

C. rubrum (Red Goosefoot): Formerly merely a ballast alien, in more recent times it tends to favour mud, e.g. at Cullalo Reservoir in 1983; and St Margaret's Hope in 1982.

Radiola linoides (Flax-seed): There are old records from near Saline (1835 Robertson) and Culross and Tulliallan (both pre-1898 White). Probably long extinct, but a very easy plant to overlook.

Geranium sylvaticum (Wood Cranesbill): Rather local, the main locality being Lethan's Den and its various subsidiary glens, 1835 (Robertson) and 1971→. Doubtfully still in 'Aberdour Woods', where the Misses Boswell mentioned it in 1820.

G. sanguineum (Bloody Cranesbill): This rare coastal plant may still be seen at North Queensferry where it was first noticed in 1836 (RBG); and at Hawkcraig, Aberdour, where Balfour listed it in the 1850/60s.

G. pyrenaicum (Pyrenean Cranesbill): Found at St Davids in the 1850s (Balfour), presumably on ballast, and by others later, and still there, 1967→. Also at Aberdour in the 1860s (Balfour).

Impatiens glandulifera (Himalayan Balsam): Together with Giant Hogweed, this is rampant by the Lyne Burn almost along its length from Dunfermline to its mouth west of Charlestown; it must have been established here long before its first recorded date of 1970. Elsewhere, occasional plants are present and it may soon become prominent by other burns.

Acer campestre (Maple): Seen first at North Queensferry in 1801 (Mackay) and at regular intervals to date since; rare in Fife, and almost certainly originally introduced.

Genista anglica (Petty Whin): Probably not infrequent formerly on the old tracts of moorland, as in the Dhu Craig (1835 Robertson)/Bogside (1911 Evans) area; Knock Hill (1846 RBG); and near Torryburn (1852 RBG). Now only in very small quantity in Tulliallan Forest, where it was first listed by Balfour in 1854, again by Buchanan in 1880 (''by no means common'') and a plant or two detected a century later.

Ulex minor (Lesser Gorse): This close relative of Whin from south England was discovered on the Forth Road Bridge cuttings (west side) in 1982 by N. F. Stewart, the first record for Fife and the second for Scotland;

possibly introduced unintentionally during the engineering operations. Also reported by the same botanist by the railway line at Culross in 1987.

Trifolium scabrum (Hard Clover): Mentioned from Inverkeithing parish in 1836 (Robertson) and found near Inverkeithing in 1954 (RBG); and near Aberdour, 1904 (Evans), which may be the Charles Hill/Port Haven shore, where it was detected in 1969. A rare plant, although easily overlooked.

T. striatum (Soft Clover): Here and there on banks facing the sea, as at the Ferry Hills, 1824 (Greville)→; and west of Rosyth Dockyard, 1982. Probably still near St Davids, where it was collected between 1849 (Balfour) and 1902 (RBG), and perhaps elsewhere.

Astragalus glycyphyllos (Wild Liquorice): Well known at the Ferry Hills, having been recorded at frequent intervals since 1794 (RBG); now in danger of disappearing, as only a few plants survive by the railway. This is one of its very few Fife stations.

Oxytropis halleri (Purple Mountain Milkvetch): One of **the** 18th century discoveries at the Ferry Hills, first mentioned in 1761 (Walker). Although present in quantity at first, e.g. MacRitchie in 1795 stated that he took ''off an abundance of excellent specimens'', predictably it grew scarcer and scarcer throughout the first half of the 19th century. Its final destruction was due to ''the process of agriculture'' (Balfour, 1855), with the last gathering in RBG dated 1860 (out of a total of 56!).

Ornithopus perpusillus (Birdsfoot): Found on the Ferry Hills in 1824 (Greville) and seen there in 1967. Inverkeithing records of 1857/66 (RBG) may refer to this site. Not easily detected, and could occur elsewhere.

Vicia lutea (Yellow Vetch): A 19th century speciality at the Ferry Hills. Recorded many times between 1802-73 (RBG), but gone by c1900, this British rarity suffered first from over-collecting (58 specimens in RBG!) and then from quarrying, including for the Forth Bridge.

Filipendula vulgaris (Dropwort): Fortunately this Scottish rarity still flourishes in its three long-known coastal sites, i.e. the Ferry Hills, 1794 (RBG)→; Donibristle/St Davids, 1820 (Boswell)→; and Hawkcraig, Aberdour, 1856 (Balfour)→. Also at Charles Hill Point, 1981 (S. J. Leach).

Rubus fruticosus agg.: Because of their variability, brambles have long caused bewilderment among botanists. However, recently much has been done to achieve order within the genus and it is now known that in Scotland there are approaching 60 species. About half that number are found in Fife, and a third in Dunfermline District; but of these 20, in turn half occur in only one or two localities.

The most common and widespread include *latifolius*, the only bramble for which there are definite old records; under the name of 'caesius' and 'corylifolius', this was listed from Kincardine in 1838 (RBG) and 1854 (Balfour), and in the North Queensferry area in 1856 (Balfour). The other very common species are *leptothyrsos*, *mucronulatus* and *nemoralis*. Still widespread, but not quite so frequent, are *infestus* and *radula*.

The following three are much more restricted in their distribution — *drejeri, errabundus* and *lindebergii*; another two are even more local, and deserving of especial mention. *Atrebatum* is a fairly recently described species from south England, which was discovered here and there in the Oakley area in 1983. *Elegantispinosus* is unknown in the wild but has been cultivated for its fruit and has escaped; it is particularly common in the Grangemouth district, and clumps are now appearing along the south coast of Fife.

In Scotland, there are four members of the Sub-Erecti group, which is the link between the rasp and the true brambles; of these, *fissus, plicatus* and *scissus* occur very sparingly, the moreso as their favoured moorland habitat disappears.

The principal station for the remaining six brambles is North Queensferry (as well as several of the above). This is not surprising when it is realised that until recently the main influx of traffic to Fife, by both road and rail, took place here, and must have been responsible for a good number of introductions. The six are *echinatoides, procerus* (an escape), *scoticus, tuberculatus, vestitus,* and *wirralensis*.

Four further species which may well yet be come across in West Fife are *laciniatus* (an ornamental escape), *pictorum, polyanthemus* and, possibly, *ulmifolius*.

R. saxatilis (Stone Bramble): There are few Fife records, and probably the sole extant one is in Lethan's Den, where it was noted several times last century, the first about 1835 (Robertson); recently, seen in 1971.

Potentilla argentea (Hoary Cinquefoil): There are three old records of this rarity — from the Ferry Hills in 1801 (? error for next species); near Crombie Point, 1853 (Balfour); and Culross, pre-1890 (White). Could the last two have been ballast introductions?

P. tabernaemontani (Spring Cinquefoil): This scarce species has long been known from the Ferry Hills, being seen first in the 1790s (RBG) and mentioned regularly since. Still present in the 1970s, although not in quantity.

P. anglica (Trailing Tormentil): A rare plant which likes forest tracks and railway lines e.g. in Tulliallan Forest, 1973→; and at Bogside, 1986→. An old Inverkeithing record of 1838 (StA) may be the same as 'Seaton', N. Queensferry, 1881 (RBG); also reported from the latter in 1954 (RBG). Its close relative *P. reptans* occurs more frequently, chiefly in the west of the District.

Poterium sanguisorba (Salad Burnet): Found in 1981 in the Roscobie area by S. J. Leach on a bank of the B914 road opposite a cottage, and reported in 1988 to occur there is some quantity (I. M. Strachan). Owing to its proximity to habitation, the possibility of introduction must be strong. The only other record is an old one from roadside between Dunfermline and Saline (1821 Hooker).

Agrimonia procera (Fragrant Agrimony): The only sighting is in the

Dunduff area, north of Dunfermline, in 1982 (N. F. Stewart); easily confused with its much more frequent relation, *A. eupatoria*.

Rosa species (Wild Rose): The roses have always caused problems in identification, although the main groups are usually readily told apart. Not a great deal of field work has yet been carried out in West Fife, but the following probably represents a reasonable picture. (It would appear that hybrids between groups, as distinct from hybrids between members of the same group, are not at all common.)

R. arvensis (Field Rose): For the record, this is planted by Pond Cottage, Culross, which is probably Evans's site of 1900, and perhaps very occasionally elsewhere.

R. pimpinellifolia (Burnet Rose): Rather local; still at the Ferry Hills, where it has been enthused over since 1821 (Greville)→. Also at St Davids; and inland, west of Ballingry. See also next species.

R. rubiginosa (Sweet Briar): Widespread, but usually only the odd bush or two; in some places, planted. Walker (1808) said in 1761 that he found 'Sweet Briar' "in some plenty" at North Ferry, but this is more likely to have referred to Burnet Rose.

R. canina group (Dog Rose): All four species occur i.e. *afzeliana, canina, coriifolia* and *dumetorum*, with the first being the most common.

R. villosa group (Downy Rose): Both *mollis* and *sherardii* are frequently to be found.

Sedum anglicum (English Stonecrop): On the shore at Downing Point, Donibristle, where it was first noticed in 1820 (Boswell); and also at Hawkcraig, Aberdour. The only other modern record for this coastal species is particularly worthy of mention, as it is about a mile inland from the last, near Parkend Farm. Also formerly near Kincardine (1836 RBG).

S. villosum (Pink Stonecrop): This is normally an upland flower, so it is regrettable that it no longer grows in the lowland Inverkeithing/Ferry Hills area, where it was found regularly from about the 1790s (RBG) to 1890 (*Edinburgh*). Neither is it extant at 'Loch Hillhead' (i.e. Black Loch, Dunduff) (1835 Robertson); however, fortunately still on the north slopes of Knock Hill/Lethan's Den area, 1850s (Balfour) and 1971.

Chrysosplenium alternifolium (Alternate Golden Saxifrage): Here and there by the Black Devon e.g. in the Little Saline area and below Balgonar; and in Gask Glen. Not seen recently at Fordel nor Woodmill (both 1835 Robertson). **Not** common, unlike its close relative, *C. oppositifolium*.

Tolmiea menziesii (Pick-a-Back Plant): Well naturalised by shady burns, as in Pittencrieff Glen, Dunfermline; and Aberdour Den, 1969→.

Parnassia palustris (Grass of Parnassus): The few records are centred around the Lethan's Den/Roscobie area, at both of which a few plants were seen in the early 1970s. Robertson mentioned it at the former about 1835 (RBG); while he also recorded it from "north of Dunfermline", which may be the Black Loch, Dunduff area, where both West and the Dunfermline Naturalists' Society admired it in 1903/05.

Drosera rotundifolia (Common Sundew): Present in scattered suitable localities e.g. near Lethan's Den, Moss Morran and Tipperton Moss, but decreasing as its habitat disappears. Also still occurs in small quantity at Din Moss, below Knock Hill, where in 1853/54 both *D. anglica* and *D. intermedia* were recorded (RBG; B and S; *Phytologist*), the latter definitely in error.

D. anglica (Great Sundew): Robertson records this from Inverkeithing Parish in 1836 (NSA), presumably from North Queensferry, where Kirkcaldy Naturalists' Society found it in the same year (Young); but these must be regarded as doubtful because none of the established botanists of the period mentioned it. See also *D. rotundifolia.*

Lythrum salicaria (Purple Loosestrife): Found at Lochgelly, 1840-70 (BM); near Dunfermline, 1840-65 (RBG); and near Aberdour, 1869 (RBG); but no 20th century records. A rare plant elsewhere in Fife and Kinross.

L. portula (Water Purslane): This small aquatic of muddy loch shores may be spreading slowly. Seen at the west pool at Lochore Meadows in 1970, and at Peppermill Dam (VC87) in 1982. An unlocalised record from Dunfermline Parish in 1844 (NSA) may have been an error.

Daphne laureola (Spurge Laurel): Noted from 'woods near Culross' as long ago as 1844 (RBG) and still at Dunimarle Castle; also well naturalised on the steep bank of Broomhall Estate between Charlestown and Limekilns, where it was observed in 1902 (RBG). Formerly at Tulliallan (1898 White).

Epilobium ciliatum (American Willowherb): The recent rapid spread of this invader has equalled that of its relative, Rosebay, earlier this century. First found in Fife in 1959, it soon reached all corners of the county. The first localised West Fife record was from the Ferry Hills in 1969. Although nearly all species of this genus are known to hybridise, in Fife most crosses involve *ciliatum*. Two West Fife taxa seen are *ciliatum* x *hirsutum* near Torrie House in 1986; and *ciliatum* x *montanum* outside Torryburn in 1986.

E. brunnescens (New Zealand Willowherb): This atypical willowherb, introduced as a rockery plant into Britain, has spread far and wide. It usually favours damp places, often as high altitudes. In West Fife, so far it is uncommon, having been detected only at Craigluscar Reservoir in 1971; and in Lethan's Den in 1982 (N. F. Stewart).

Hippurus vulgaris (Marestail): Not now in some of its old haunts, but still at Loch Fitty, 1905 (West)→; and on Benarty; at Lochore Meadows; at Lumphinnans; and one or two other suitable stations.

Anthriscus caucalis (Bur Chervil): Of a few early records, only that at Port Laing (N. Queensferry) seems still to be a current site; first seen there in 1853 (Balfour). Could persist at Aberdour (1839 RBG) and in Culross area (pre-1890 White).

Smyrnium olusatrum (Alexanders): Rather surprisingly, there is only one record for this old pot-herb i.e. outside Culross, where it probably grew well before it was first noticed in 1912 (*Edinburgh*) and where it continues to flourish.

Oenanthe fistulosa (Water Dropwort): This Scottish rarity was listed as long ago as 1768 by Hope "in moist ground . . . at North Ferry" and a decade later "in ditches and rivulets between Inverkeithing and North Ferry" (Lightfoot et al). It seems to have disappeared by the end of the 18th century; there is one later, undated, specimen from "near Dunfermline" in RBG. Known now in Fife from only one station.

Meum athamanticum (Spignel or Baldmoney): Formerly at Lochend, north of Dunfermline, in the 1850s (Balfour/RBG); and at Pitdinnie Farm, Cairneyhill in 1866 (BSE). It must have occurred elsewhere, but as agricultural improvements increased, it correspondingly decreased and has in all probability disappeared.

Apium inundatum (Marshwort): There are a scattering of old records, the only extant of which is Cullalo, where West saw it in 1905. Noted recently in the Tulliallan area, both in the Castle pond and at Keir's Dam; and at Peppermill Dam and Moor Loch.

Apium graveolens (Wild Celery): There were several records from the salt-marsh west of Culross between 1834 (Robertson) and 1874 (*Reports of the Botanical Exchange Club*); White (1898) considered it to be an outcast. Now, it is the very similar (but poisonous) *Oenanthe crocata* which flourishes at this spot.

Cicuta virosa (Cowbane): This poisonous plant has been known since 1821 (Hooker) at Otterston Loch, still being there in 1969; needs to be monitored, as it has not been seen lately in this, its only extant VC85 locality. Formerly at Black Loch, Dunduff, from 1835 (Robertson) to 1862 (Balfour).

Patinaca sativa (Wild Parsnip): Probably originally introduced with ballast at both St Davids, 1837 (RBG) and Inverkeithing, 1849 (RBG) and long thoroughly naturalised. Also seen recently below the Forth Road Bridge at North Queensferry.

Heracleum mantegazzianum (Giant Hogweed): This escape, which really deserves the name of 'giant,' has reached pest proportions along almost the whole length of the Lyne Burn from Dunfermline to Waukmill; also at the west end of Rosyth Dockyard. First recorded in 1957, but obviously present long before then.

H. mantegazzianum x *sphondylium*: Where the two parents grow together, there is a chance they will cross, and this proved to be the case near the Lyne Burn south of Crossford in 1979, when one or two plants with intermediate characters were discovered.

Torilis nodosa (Knotted Bur Parsley): About 1835 Robertson listed this from the Ferry Hills, but as there is no other record, this may have been an error; easily confused with *Anthriscus caucalis*, which does grow there.

Polygonum viviparum (Alpine Bistort): Formerly on the Ferry Hills, 1830-49 (RBG); as it was reported to occur "very sparingly", the 35 spikes gathered in 1849 were not exactly a conservation measure! Luckily, still to be observed in the Lethan's Den area, 1835 (Robertson)→; and on the west end of the Cleish Hills; but unlikely now to be found on

Knock Hill (1857 Balfour).

Rumex alpinus (Monk's Rhubarb): Previously planted by country cottages, and still occasionally flourishing where they remain; and also well naturalised by burns, especially in Kinross-shire. In West Fife, the only known extant locality is in the Lethan's Den area, where it has been known since the 1840/50s (Balfour/RBG)→; and seen at Midfield Farm, Steelend, in 1973 (A. Mason).

Parietaria judaica (Wall Pellitory): Mentioned from several spots in years gone by, and still present at most, including Inverkeithing, 1795 (MacRitchie)→; Aberdour, 1820 (Boswell)→; Culross, 1839 (NSA)→; and Tulliallan, 1854/80 (Balfour;Buchanan)→.

Myrica gale (Bog Myrtle): In 1768, Hope stated "it is not nearer to Edinb. yn Aberdour" and there are several subsequent records from the Aberdour area, including "abundantly" in 1824 (Woodforde). Now, there are only half-a-dozen scrawny plants on Moss Easy, one of only two remaining Fife localities. In 1901, Evans noted "2 or 3 plants" west of Culross, which may have been the Sands Quarry of Buchanan 20 years earlier.

Salix spp. (Willow): Because of planting and the tendency of most species to hybridise, most older willow records are rather confused. Therefore, all taxa seen in West Fife are listed, in alphabetical order, species followed by hybrids. An opinion as to status and frequency is given, and some locations. Most hybrids have been determined by R. D. Meikle.

S. alba (White Willow): Common; planted and seldom self-sown.

S. aurita (Eared Willow): Common and widespread; native.

S. caprea (Goat Willow): Very common; native, perhaps planted here and there.

S. cinerea (Sallow): Common; native, probably all ssp. *oleifolia*.

S. fragilis (Crack Willow): Widely planted; the vars. *decipiens* and *russelliana* are about equally common.

S. myrsinifolia (Dark Willow): Rare, native; seen only in Lethan's Den and Roughcleugh Den area. (The closely related *S. phylicifolia* does not seem to occur.)

S. pentandra (Bay Willow): Occasionally planted, possibly self-sown. Grows at Cowstrandburn; Devilla Forest; Dean Plantation, west of Dunfermline; and on Comrie Pit bing (N. F. Stewart).

S. purpurea (Purple Willow): Planted locally, as at Otterston Loch; Loch Fitty; Cowstrandburn; etc.

S. repens (Creeping Willow): Occasional, probably decreasing, native; still on Din Moss (by Knock Hill), where Balfour saw it in 1852. The 'Dunfermline' record in 1863 (B and S) may refer to Dean Plantation, where it is to be found; also at Black Loch, Dunduff; etc. The ssp. is *repens*.

S. viminalis (Osier): Widely planted and self-propagated, appearing native.

S. alba x *fragilis*: Rare; planted at Otterston Loch.

S. aurita x *cinerea*: Occasional, as at Black Loch, Dunduff; and west of Saline in Dun Moss area; native.

S. aurita x *repens*: Rare, native; in Dean Plantation, west of Dunfermline.

S. caprea x *cinerea*: Native; almost certainly more common than the two localised records, at North Queensferry and Blairadam, indicate.

S. cinerea x *viminalis*: Planted here and there, e.g. at Cullalo; near Inverkeithing; etc.

S. purpurea x *viminalis*: Rarely planted, as at Otterston Loch.

S. x *stipularis*: Frequently planted; flourishes at Craigluscar; by the Black Devon; by the Dour Burn; etc.

Vaccinium vitis-idaea (Cowberry): Rather rare, the only definite locality being by the Bluther Burn at Bath Moor — the 'Dhu Craig' station of 1835 (Robertson). Could still be in Lethan's Den, where Robertson also saw it; and the Tulliallan area, 1854 (Balfour).

V. oxycoccus (Cranberry): May yet be found where sphagnum bogs have been allowed to remain, as on Din Moss (Knock Hill), 1852 (Balfour)→ (though now threatened by recent planting); Moss Morran, east side, 1919 (Templeman)→; Dun Moss, west of Saline, 1973→; and Culross Moor, 1972→; etc. Apparently no longer at Otterston Loch, 1809 (Maughan) to 1837 (RBG).

Pyrola minor (Wintergreen): The three wintergreens are notoriously difficult to separate, especially when non-flowering. Only *P. minor* has been seen in recent years and it seems best to consider all old records under one head. All three were reported from the banks of the Black Devon, i.e. Lethan's Den area, in the 1840/50s (Balfour) but there are no 20th century records. Other old localities include Culross (pre- 1890 White); Tulliallan woods (1853 Balfour); and Blackcleugh Glen, 1848 (RBG). Modern sightings of *P. minor* are from the SW part of Moss Morran, 1983; near Goat Quarry, 1984 (S. J. Leach); and Inzievar estate Oakley, 1982.

P. media and *P. rotundifolia*: see *P. minor*.

Primula veris (Cowslip): Probably now exclusively coastal; still to be admired at various places between Limekilns and Aberdour, as west of Rosyth Castle, where it was "abundant" in 1834 (Dewar); the Ferry Hills, 1834 (RBG)→; etc. Its hybrid with *P. vulgaris* ('*P. elatior*') was recorded from several sites in the 19th century but there are no recent sightings.

Lysimachia vulgaris (Yellow Loosestrife): Known from Loch Gelly since 1863 (B and S)→; and at Otterston Loch, 1880 (RBG)→. Formerly near Dunfermline and Donibristle, both 1863 (B and S). Pretty certainly an introduction.

Trientalis europaea (Chickweed Wintergreen): Widespread and locally common; still present in several of its old localities, including Townhill Wood, Dunfermline, 1835 (Graham; RBG)→; Lethan's Moor, 1839 (Campbell)→; Carnock Moor, Clune, 1843 (NSA)→; Lundin Wood near Crossford, 1898 (Evans)→; etc.

Samolus valerandi (Brookweed): Discovered about the turn of the 18th century at Limekilns, and near Dunfermline, while there is an undated specimen from North Queensferry (all RBG). As these long past records are the sole ones from Fife, the plant has not been seen in the county for approaching two centuries.

Gentianella campestris (Field Gentian): Listed in 1824 (Woodforde) at the Ferry Hills, and still there; reported as being a "a thriving colony" in 1982 (S. J. Leach). There is also an old record from Aberdour dated 1865 (RBG).

Cynoglossum officinale (Houndstongue): Mentioned from the coast at Rosyth Castle, 1835-51, and Donibristle, 1835-53 (Roberston; Balfour); and Aberdour, 1863 (B and S), but no later records. (A few plants still grow along the east coast of Fife.)

Symphytum officinale (Common Comfrey): The Inverkeithing area is the stronghold of this plant, rare in Fife, flourishing in several sites, e.g. by the Inverkeithing Burn, 1835 (Robertson)→; near Charlestown, 1850 (Balfour)→; and in Dunfermline, 1895 (Evans)→; etc. Both white and purple vars. occur; not to be confused with the widespread hybrid, *S. x uplandicum.*

Pentaglottis sempervirens (Evergreen Alkanet): A tenacious garden species which will persist for many years if it escapes, as at Aberdour Castle, 1820 (Boswell)→; west of Culross, 1835 (Robertson)→; etc.

Atropa belladonna (Deadly Nightshade): There are several old records including "betwixt Culross and Torryburn" in 1724 (Blair); Limekilns and Charlestown, 1821 (Greville) to 1866 (Balfour); near Crombie Point, 1824 (Woodforde) to 1896 (Young); and Donibristle, 1835 (Robertson) to 1905 (RBG). However, no recent sightings have been reported.

Limosella aquatica (Mudwort): After having virtually disappeared from Scotland, this inconspicuous plant was found by Loch Leven in 1973, and subsequently by several Fife lochs. When the natural part of Cullalo Reservoir was drained for a time in 1982 and 1983, it appeared in quantity there on the exposed mud.

Veronica montana (Wood Speedwell): A West Fife speciality, as there are very few other Fife records. Perhaps surprisingly there are no old records, for it is locally common in both Dunimarle woods and Blair Castle den; at Shaw Hill wood, near Torrie House; and by Bluther Burn near High Valleyfield (N. F. Stewart).

V. filiformis (Slender Speedwell): This invader of lawns, parks, verges, etc, was first noted in West Fife in 1962 at Culross (RBG) and is now widespread, including at Aberdour Cemetery; Fordell; Limekilns; etc.

Pedicularis sylvatica (Lousewort): Very local in damp woodland, as in the Cadgerford area, west of Saline; and in the upper part of Lethan's Den. No longer at Dalgety, nor on the "moor west of Aberdour" (probably the same locality), 1836/49 (RBG).

Melampyrum pratense (Common Cow-Wheat): Probably not infrequent in the past, but the only recorded instances are from Lethan's Den in 1834 where it was "most abundant" (Dewar/RBG) and where it happily still occurs, although much reduced; and between Kincardine and Culross, 1850 (Balfour).

Euphrasia ssp. (Eyebright): Comparatively few species of this difficult group grow in Fife, those occurring in Dunfermline District being:—

arctica, ssp. *borealis*: much the commonest eyebright.

confusa: scattered, rather local, often on hills.

nemerosa: apparently not common.

scottica: rare in flushes and damp ground, as in Lethan's Den and Moss Morran.

Lathraea squamaria (Toothwort): A Fife rarity, as the only locality is Lethan's Den, where it was espied in 1978; however, as this plant is difficult to detect, it could occur in one or two other spots.

Orobanche alba (Thyme Broomrape): Discovered on the cliffs near St Davids about 1820 (RBG), and "fine specimens" admired there in 1840 (*BSE*). Reported still present in the late 1960s (J. Carlyle).

Pinguicula vulgaris (Butterwort): Not infrequent in suitable habitats elsewhere in Fife, but in the west of the county found recently only in the Lethan's Den area in 1971. May still be on Moss Morran, where it was collected in 1883 (RBG).

Origanum vulgare (Marjoram): Known since 1837 (RBG) at Hawkcraig, Aberdour and still there, one of its few Fife stations.

Nepeta cataria (Wild Catmint): There are two very old records, from North Ferry in 1768 (Hope); and roadside between Culross and Kincardine in 1821 (Hooker). If correct, both were probably introductions (cf.1863 B and S); in 1880 Buchanan stated "not now found".

Clinopodium vulgare (Wild Basil): The sole known extant site is Hawkcraig, Aberdour, where it has been observed since 1820 (Boswell). Old stations include near Dunfermline and Cullalo Hills, both 1835 (Robertson); and Ferry Hills (1836 Graham; Dewar corr.)

Stachys arvensis (Field Woundwort): A rare weed of lighter soils, recently seen only at the Ferry Hills, where it seems to have persisted since 1794 (RBG). May occur here and there elsewhere.

Ballota nigra (Black Horehound): Long known at St Davids, where Robertson saw it about 1835 and where it still occurs, as it does at Brucehaven, where it was found in 1863 (B and S). Not seen recently at North Queensferry, where Robertson also recorded it, as did Christie in 1901 (RBG), but noted at Charles Hill Point in 1981 (S. J. Leach).

Scutellaria galericulata (Skullcap): In 1905, West stated this grew "in marshy ground adjoining the seashore, about 2 miles S.W. of Aberdour, in great abundance", which is presumably the "shore near Donibristle" where Fraser also saw it in 1905 (RBG). West also mentioned Cullalo Reservoir, and fortunately it still survives there, its only West Fife locality.

Sherardia arvensis (Field Madder): Very local on dry banks or waste ground. Found on the Ferry Hills at intervals since 1847 (RBG) and probably still there, especially as it was seen nearby in 1982; and at Charles Hill Point (both N. F. Stewart).

Galium mollugo (Hedge Bedstraw): This is very thinly scattered throughout Fife; the only extant record in the west of the county is from Hillend in 1970 (ssp. *erectum*), which may be the St Davids, 1889 (RBG) and/or Dalgety, 1919 (Templeman) sites.

Sambucus ebulus (Dwarf Elder): Known from Inverkeithing for nearly two centuries, having been first found in 1794 (RBG), the only extant Fife locality. There are two close-by sites, by both main and branch railway lines near the tunnel.

Viburnum opulus (Guelder Rose): Recorded as far back as 1855 from Lethan's Den area by J. H. Balfour and so may be native there, where it still flourishes; elsewhere, occasionally planted.

Adoxa moschatellina (Moschatel): This dainty but easily overlooked spring flower was noted from the Culross area about 1835 (Robertson), and may still be detected at Dunimarle and near Blair Castle. Also by the Bluther Burn at Low Valleyfield; by the Black Devon near Little Saline, and in Comrie Dean.

Valerianella locusta (Cornsalad): Seemingly rare, being found currently on the coast only at Aberdour, 1969→. Quite possibly still on the Ferry Hills and near Limekilns, but not seen at either since 1835 (Robertson).

Bidens cernua (Nodding Bur Marigold): Old stations are Fordell (1835 Robertson); Otterston Loch and near Rosyth Castle (1863 B and S); probably long extinct. A close relative *B. tripartita* has also been recorded but was probably merely a ballast alien.

Senecio aquaticus (Marsh Ragwort): There are two old records, from north of Dunfermline (1835 Robertson); and near Aberdour (1848 RBG); but none since. Rare in Fife and Kinross, the nearest site being Loch Leven.

S. squalidus (Oxford Ragwort): The spread of this invader throughout England and into Scotland has been well documented; in West Fife, it crops up here and there in small quantity, as at St Davids in 1969; Charlestown in 1970; and Inverkeithing in 1986. It seems odd it was not recorded at these sites as a ballast alien 150 years ago.

S. vernalis (Spring Ragwort): A very recent newcomer to the Fife flora, being found for the first time at Dalgety Bay in 1982 (O. M. Stewart). May well spread further afield in years to come.

Doronicum pardalianches (Leopardsbane): Introduced many years ago and thoroughly naturalised, e.g. at Dunimarle, Culross, where it was first noticed in 1821 (Hooker) and where it is now more or less dominant. Also near Otterston Loch, 1866 (RBG)→; Fordell, 1969→; etc.

D. plantagineum (Leopardsbane): Much less common than the previous species. The only current station is at Dunimarle, Culross (with the last), where it was first observed about 1880 (Buchanan). The variety is *willdenovii*.

Petasites hybridus (Butterbur): Although fairly frequent in other parts of the county, the only known West Fife site is at the mouth of the Dour Burn, where it was first seen in 1864 (Balfour).

P. albus (White Butterbur): There are no old records, which is a little surprising as this species seems to have been well established in several places for a long time, e.g. about the site of Valleyfield House;

below the Bluther Burn viaduct; and near Craigluscar Farm.

P. fragrans (Winter Heliotrope): An escape or cast-out which readily colonises ground, e.g. below the Forth Road Bridge; at Crombie Point; and in Pitreavie Castle grounds. A large colony near Inverkeithing Station, known since 1912 (*Edinburgh*) has survived recent building in its immediate vicinity.

Filago vulgaris (Common Cudweed): Formerly on the Ferry Hills, 1835 (Robertson) to 1872 (Balfour); and in the Inverkeithing/St Davids area, 1848/9 (RBG). Could still occur perhaps at the former station.

F. mimima (Small Cudweed): There are old records from Culross (1840 RBG); Ferry Hills (1835 Robertson); and Aberdour (1864 RBG). The only modern stations are on coastal waste ground at Newmills, 1981; near Culross, 1984; and on Blairhall and Comrie Pit bings, 1985 (N. F. Stewart).

Gnaphalium sylvaticum (Heath Cudweed): in recent years seen in small quantity only by forest tracks at Cullalo and Benarty, both in 1969. Previously at the Ferry Hills (1835 Robertson); and Dunfermline (1863 B and S).

Antennaria dioica (Mountain Everlasting). Formerly at the Ferry Hills from 1794 (Mackay) to 1856 (Balfour); and on Knock Hill in 1852 (Balfour); probably extinct for some time.

Solidago virgaurea (Goldenrod): Apparently rare, there being only two modern records, from Benarty in 1982 (N. F. Stewart), and west of Bath Moor, in 1983 (S. J. Leach). May still be in the vicinity of Aberdour (1865 RBG); St Davids (1902 RBG); Culross (1835/80 Robertson/Buchanan); and perhaps elsewhere.

Eupatorium cannabinum (Hemp Agrimony): There are two old coastal records, from Aberdour, 1820 (Boswell) to 1847 (RBG); and near St Davids, 1835 (Robertson) to c1900 (Evans). Conceivably may still occur.

Artemisia absinthium (Wormwood): Still persists near the shore at North Queensferry, where Mackay saw it in 1794; but seems to be have disappeared from the St Davids/Donibristle area, where he also recorded it, as did Balfour in 1849. Formerly also at Kincardine (1838 RBG) and Culross (pre-1898 White).

Carduus tenuiflorus (Seaside Thistle): Found near Inverkeithing from 1835 (Robertson) to 1890 (*Glasgow*); and at North Queensferry in 1849/56 (Balfour); could still occur, but not seen recently. Also at St Davids, 1857-1913 (RBG) but here possibly a ballast alien.

C. helenoides (Melancholy Thistle): Found in 1835 by Robertson in Lethan's Den and still there, and in nearby Milton Dean, 1971→. Also on both sides of the Fife/Kinross border at the Kelty Burn, 1982→.

Mycelis muralis (Wall Lettuce): Scattered here and there, as at Aberdour, where it was first seen in 1902 (RBG); in the old quarries at Charlestown; and at Dalgety Bay.

Hieracium spp. (Hawkweed): This is a notoriously difficult genus, and superficial investigations only have been made so far in Fife. In the west, two broad groups may be listed, namely weeds and those which occur on rocks. Much the commonest in the first category is *vulgatum*, followed by *perpropinquum* and occasionally *salticola* and *subcrocatum*, and possibly *vagum*. Of those in rocky places the most interesting is *dewarii*, described from material collected in 1844 from Lethan's Den by A. Dewar, and still present. Also in that locality is *rubiginosum*; while *schmidtii* has been found at the Saline Hills, and *subrude* at North Queensferry. *Grandidens* grows here and there on walls in towns.

Taraxacum spp. (Dandelion): Although some field work has been carried out in other parts of Fife and Kinross to determine which micro-species occur, none has yet been done in West Fife.

Baldellia ranunculoides (Lesser Water Plantain): There are two records, both dating back some 150 years: Black Loch, Dunduff (1835 Robertson) and Otterston Loch (1838 StA). This plant is almost certainly extinct in Fife.

Zostera spp. (Eelgrass): This is a difficult group, but the determination of *Z. "nana"*, i.e. *noltii*, from Torryburn Bay in the 1880s by Evans (*BSE*) seems correct — it was carpeting the mud there 100 years later. In nearby Culross Bay, N. F. Stewart considered that both *noltii* and *angustifolia* were present in 1982. An Aberdour record of 1865 of "*Z. marina*" (RBG) awaits expert identification.

Potamogeton spp. (Pondweed): Owing to the threats to water bodies in general and to reservoirs in particular, details of all the true pondweeds are given, in alphabetical order. It is salutary to read George West's survey issued in 1910 to find out the changes there have been since then.

P. alpinus (Reddish Pondweed): Not seen recently in Loch Fitty, where West found it to be "abundant" in 1905; nor in Loch Gelly's effluent.

P. berchtoldii (Slender Pondweed): In Otterston Loch in 1869/71 (BM), and still there over a century later; and at Craigluscar, which may be the 1888 "pool near Dunfermline" site (*Glasgow*). Present in most lochs, and not uncommon.

P. crispus (Curled Pondweed): Not specifically seen in some of its old stations, e.g. Otterston (1835 Robertson); Loch Gelly (1835 Robertson); nor Black Loch, Dunduff (1852 Balfour); but could still be present in all three. Grows at Lochore Meadows; Craigluscar; pond at Lumphinnans; etc. Locally frequent.

P. filiformis (Slender Pondweed): Found in Loch Gelly from 1868 (BM) to 1905 (West); and at Cullalo and Loch Fitty, 1905 (West), but not detected in any of these recently. The only current locality is Craigluscar, but it could occur elsewhere. Uncommon.

P. gramineus (Various-leaved Pondweed): There are a handful of old records, including Loch Gelly (1820 Boswell); Loch Fitty (1835 Robertson); Carnock Moor (1843 Dewar); and Black Loch, Dunduff (1863 B and S). Seen at none of these this century, and presumably extinct (although still present in other Fife districts).

P. lucens (Shining Pondweed): There are three old records, but no current ones; formerly in Loch Gelly 1820/35 (Boswell;Robertson); Dunfermline

(1863 B and S); and Cullalo (1905 West). Not seen recently at all in Fife and Kinross, so may be extinct in VC85.

P. natans (Broad-leaved Pondweed): The commonest pondweed, present in both deep and shallow water (including ditches). The "near Culross" record of 1866 (RBG) may be Keirs Dam (Tulliallan Forest), where it is was seen in 1972. Still at Loch Fitty, where West saw it in 1905; etc.

P. obtusifolius (Blunt-leaved Pondweed): Balfour came across this in Black Loch, Dunduff, in 1852; and West collected it from both Cullalo and Loch Fitty ("abundant") in 1905. Seen at none of these sites recently (although may still be present); but at Craigluscar; in a pool at Loch Gelly in the 1970s; and in Keirs Dam (Tulliallan Forest) in 1985 (N. F. Stewart). Uncommon.

P. pectinatus (Fennel Pondweed): Flourishes in suitable sites in the eastern part of the District, including Town Loch, which may be the "near Dunfermline" record of 1863 (B and S); and at lochs Fitty and Gelly, where West collected it in 1905. Also in Cullalo; Lochore Meadows; etc. Locally common.

P. perfoliatus (Perfoliate Pondweed): Not detected for many years at Loch Gelly (1820/35 Boswell/Robertson); but still in Dunfermline (Town Loch), where it was noted in 1863 (B and S) and Loch Fitty, 1905 (West). Also at Craigluscar; etc. Locally common.

P. polygonifolius (Bog Pondweed): Not uncommon in acid bogs and pools, never in deeper water. Not now at the Ferry Hills (1863 B and S) nor Loch Fitty (1905 West); but on Craigluscar Hill; Benarty; etc.

P. pusillus (Lesser Pondweed): In Loch Gelly last century (1835 Robertson and 1869 BM), but not seen since. Neither is it at Cullalo (1905 West); but still in Loch Fitty (ditto). Also in Craigluscar; Lochore Meadows; etc. Rather local.

P. praelongus (Long-stalked Pondweed): One of Fife's rarest extant pondweeds; in Dunfermline District, now found only at Craigluscar; seemingly gone from Cullalo and Loch Fitty (both 1905 West).

P. x zizii: West discovered this hybrid in 1905 in three lochs, Cullalo, Otterston and Fitty, in the last being reported as "abundant". Eighty years later, only very little was present at Fitty, and none at all in the other two stations. Very rare.

Zannichellia palustris (Horned Pondweed): Occasional in fresh-water, as at Otterston Loch, where West noted it in 1905; Loch Gelly; and Lochore Meadows.

Narthecium ossifragum (Bog Asphodel): May still be found where bogs persist, e.g. at Din Moss, which may be the 1857 Saline Hills record (Macmillan); Moss Morran; Tipperton Moss (Cleish Hills); Benarty; etc.

Tulipa sylvestris (Wild Tulip): Known since the 1850s (Balfour; B and S) "behind the stables at Donibristle", where presumably it had been introduced. A shy flowerer, 21 blooms were seen here in 1969, but none in 1982; however, nearby, east of Donibristle House, 9 flowers were seen in the same spring, among trees.

Allium scorodoprasum (Sand Leek): Still occurs on the coast in the Doni-
bristle/St Davids area, where it was known before 1835 (Robertson);
and also at Culross, since before 1900 (Evans)→.

A. vineale (Crow Garlic): A coastal species, known from several localities
east from the Ferry Hills, 1835 (Robertson)→; St Davids/Donibristle,
1820 (Boswell)→; to Aberdour, 1828 (RBG)→.

A. paradoxum (Siberian Garlic): Found in Aberdour harbour area in 1969,
the only locality; as it is increasing its range in Fife and Kinross, it is
only a matter of time before it is seen — and smelt! — elsewhere.

A. ursinum (Broad-leaved Garlic): Common, often dominant in dens, as
in Aberdour Den; Lethan's Den; etc. An unusual seaside site is near
Port Laing, North Queensferry, where it was first noted in 1849 (RBG).

Paris quadrifolia (Herb Paris): There are several 19th century records but
none since. This is in common with reported decreases elsewhere, but
as it has been refound here and there recently outwith Fife, it may
turn up again. Mentioned from Lethan's Den 1835-58 (Robertson; RBG;
Campbell — "pervades a whole wood"); Culross 1835 (Robertson),
i.e. Blair Castle/Dunimarle 1863/1901 (B and S; Evans); woods at
Tulliallan 1850s (Balfour); and Blackcleughburn Glen 1848 (RBG).

Juncus tenuis. (Slender Rush): Although now not uncommon in other parts
of Scotland, this invader has yet to colonise Fife. One of the only two
records to date is just within the county boundary near Solsgirth Mine
in 1981.

Luzula nivea (Whitish Woodrush): In 1846 this caused some excitement
when A. Dewar came across it in Broomhall Estate and described it
as being "unquestionably wild". However, it was soon ascertained
that it had been planted (see *BSE Proceedings; Phytologist*); in 1919,
Templeman refound it. A close relative, *L. luzuloides* , was also collected
from Broomhall in the 1850s (RBG); and in Valleyfield House grounds
1905/12 (RBG). Neither has been rediscovered recently, but they could
still persist.

Galanthus nivalis (Snowdrop): Well naturalised in many woods and still
flourishing near Culross (at Dunimarle); and near Saline (at Bandrum)
where Robertson found this winter favourite 150 years ago.

Narcissus pseudo-narcissus (Wild Daffodil): There are several 19th century
records from the neighbourhood of Culross commencing in 1821
(Hooker); and there is still a good colony off the main road in Blair
Castle grounds; also present in Broomhall policies. In both cases
originally introduced, but not to be mistaken for the various cultivated
varieties which are planted or cast out and more or less naturalised
in many places.

Cephalanthera longifolia (Narrow Helleborine): The only record for Fife
is at Leckerstone, Broomhall, from where there are three mentions in
the early 1840s — by Dewar, Young and Graham. As this is one of
the few Scottish localities for this national rarity, it is indeed
unfortunate that it is almost certainly extinct there.

Epipactis helleborine (Common Helleborine): Scattered here and there, seemingly thriving reasonably well in its old haunts, as near Torryburn, 1853 (Balfour) and 1979 (B. J. Coppins); the old Valleyfield House area, pre-1890 (White) and 1979; near Oakley, 1871 (Kew) and 1982 (J. Crichton); Muir Dean (Fordell area), 1919 (Templeman) and 1986; and in Broomhall Estate, 1977→.

Listera ovata (Common Twayblade): Still reasonably common. Present in the Donibristle area, where Robertson first mentioned it about 1835; also at Inzievar, Oakley; Broomhall; and Cuttlehill near Crossgates.

L. cordata (Lesser Twayblade): Observed by Robertson and Dewar in a "wood between Dunfermline and Culross" about 1835 "in small quantity". This unhelpful description is unlikely to have been "Knock Hill near Dunfermline", as listed in 1863 (B and S), the only other locality. Probably long extinct.

Neottia nidus-avis (Birdsnest Orchid): The only known locality is in Broomhall Estate, where it was seen in 1919 (Young) and where it was refound in small quantity in 1984 by S. J. Leach. Could occur elsewhere as it is easily overlooked.

Hammarbya paludosa (Bog Orchid): Detected on the Ferry Hills in the 1830s (Dewar/RBG/etc); and in bogs in the Hillside-Powmill area in 1857 (Macmillan). May just conceivably still occur in the latter but unlikely, which is a pity as there are no 20th century Fife records.

Corallorhiza trifida (Coralroot Orchid): There were apparently at least three localities for this species, the best known being "woods near Culross" from 1835 (Robertson; Dewar) to 1866, when it was noted as abundant (*BSE*). J. H. Balfour also has "woods at Tulliallan", 1853/66, which may be connected with the "Kincardine Station" of White. I. B. Balfour found it in the late 19th century in the Solsgirth area (Evans). Unfortunately, it does not seem to have been seen this century.

Coeloglossum viride (Frog Orchid): There are several old records but none for over a century, so this orchid must be considered extinct in West Fife. Formerly on the Ferry Hills, 1768 to 1849 (Hope; Balfour); in Black Loch area, Dunduff (1835 Robertson; B and S); Aberdour (1848 RBG); Tulliallan area (1854 Balfour); and Knock Hill (1857 RBG).

Gymnadenia conopsea (Fragrant Orchid): There is a sprinkling of old records but, regrettably, no recent ones. In the past at Aberdour (1820 Boswell); Ferry Hills (1824/35 Greville/Robertson); by the Black Devon (1835 Robertson to 1857 Balfour); Knock Hill (1857 RBG); Sheriffs Dene (1854 StA); and Kincardine (1860 Balfour).

Pseudorchis albida (Small White Orchid): This delicate orchid has, sadly, not been espied in Fife for over a century. It was first found on the Ferry Hills in 1824 (Greville) and last collected in 1872 (StA). It was seen "in large quantities" in Lethan's Den in the 1830s (Robertson; Dewar; Campbell) and gathered in the 1850s there by Balfour; and at Knock Hill from 1848 (RBG) to 1874 (*BSE*).

Platanthera bifolia and *P. chlorantha* (Butterfly Orchid): These two species are very alike, and some early botanists did not always differentiate them; while others recorded both from the same site. *P. bifolia* now seems to be very rare in Fife and Kinross (only two known stations), wheras *P. chlorantha* is widespread although by no means common. Old stations for both orchids are Dun Moss, west of Saline (1872 Kew); Lethan's Den area (1835-66 Robertson; Balfour; etc); Tulliallan (1854 Balfour); and Knock Hill (1857 RBG). Recent sites for *P. chlorantha* include roadside west of Saline; Roughcleugh Glen; Roscobie Reservoir; etc.

Orchis mascula (Early Purple Orchid): Very local, although perhaps overlooked a little. May still be at the Ferry Hills, where it occurred between 1835 (Robertson) to 1852 (Balfour). In Lethan's Den; on Benarty; and at Gowkhall and Calais (A. Mason), all in the 1970s.

Anacamptis pyramidalis (Pyramidal Orchid): Mentioned from North Queensferry by Chalmers (1859), but this would appear to be an error as there is no other record from here.

Sparganium emersum (Small Bur-reed): This species and *S. ramosum* tend to run into each other and are not always easy to differentiate. It definitely occurs at the inflow to Cullalo Reservoir, where Evans found it in 1900 (RBG); and probably elsewhere, including some of its other reported 'stations, e.g. Loch Gelly (1820 Boswell); Loch Glow (1882 RBG); and lochs Fitty and Otterston (1905 West).

S. angustifolium (Floating Bur-reed): There is a handful of old records, including Black Loch, Dunduff (1835 Robertson); Aberdour, ?Otterston (1837 Young); Knock Hill and Loch Fitty, both 1857 (RBG); and Craigluscar (1919 Templeman). Recently seen only at Loch Glow in 1981→.

S. minimum (Least Bur-reed): The sole report is from Craigluscar in 1919 by Templeman, with *S. angustifolium*.

Trichophorum cespitosum (Deer-Grass): Decreasing as moorland is reclaimed, but may still be found on lower parts of the Saline Hills, where Robertson saw it about 1835; at Moss Morran; Cleish Hills; and Lockshaw Moss.

Eleocharis quinqueflora (Few-flowered Spikerush): There are old records from the "side of Inverkeithing Bay" (c1800 RBG); North Queensferry (1856/58 Balfour); and Aberdour (1863 B and S). The only modern site is far removed from these, at Benarty in 1980 (S. J. Leach).

E. multicaulis (Many-stalked Spikerush): Old records from "near Dunfermline" of the 1830/40s (Robertson; Dewar; Balfour etc.) almost certainly refer to Craigluscar and/or Carnock Moor. There are no 20th century records from these places, nor indeed from anywhere else in Fife.

E. acicularis (Needle Spikerush): Although occurring at other suitable stations in Fife, there are no recent records. Previously, at Loch Gelly (1835 to 1870 Robertson; BM); North Queensferry (1840 RBG); and Loch Fitty (1905 West).

Scirpus sylvaticus (Wood Clubrush): There is a scattering of old records, only one of which has been refound, at Otterston where West saw it in 1905. Other recent sites are Dalgety Bay, near the shore; and at Hilton of Beath pond. Probably occurs elsewhere, especially westwards.

Blysmus rufus (Chestnut sedge): Gathered on many occasions from the shore west of Aberdour by Balfour's students between 1840-70, and still there in 1911 (Evans); but not recorded since. There is also a pre-1890 mention from Longannet (White).

Schoenoplectus lacustris (Bulrush): Occasional by the shores of lochs, as at both Black Loch, Dunduff, and Loch Fitty, where Robertson saw it about 1835; the very closely related *S. tabernaemontani* may occur at both as well; and also at Hilton of Beath pond (S. J. Leach). The latter was seen near Culross before 1898 (White).

Isolepis setacea (Bristle Clubrush): Rare in open damp ground, as near Solsgirth Mine; near Steelend, Saline; Craigencat, Cleish Hills; and Peppermill Dam (N. F. Stewart). An old station is Kincardine (1850 RBG).

Eleogiton fluitans (Floating Spikerush): Present in the pond on the Ferry Hills from 1867 (RBG) to 1909 (Evans), but no later record. One of the very few modern Fife records is from Moor Loch, Tulliallan (VC87), in 1982 (N. F. Stewart).

Carex spp. (Sedge): These are mostly denizens of wet ground and because their habitat is fast diminishing, all species recorded from West Fife are listed, in alphabetical order.

C. acutiformis (Lesser Pond Sedge): Still at Otterston Loch, where it was found in 1820 (Boswell); and in Lethan's Den, where it was collected in 1838 (RBG). Also at Loch Fitty, 1980→. Rather local.

C. aquatilis (Water Sedge): East central Scotland is the headquarters of this species, which was often mis-identified last century. Seen in 1840 (Dewar) in Dunfermline, probably at Town Loch, where it still occurs; and at Loch Fitty in 1862 by Balfour and in 1905 by West, both of whom remarked on its abundance there (and which still is the case). Also at Cullalo and Roscobie Reservoirs; and at Loch Gelly. Locally common.

C. arenaria (Sand Sedge): Although frequent in East Fife in suitable habitats, the only stations west of Burntisland are at Aberdour's Silver Sands, where it was seen by Balfour in 1858; and west of Dalgety Bay, where Fraser found it in 1905. Rare.

C. binervis (Moor Sedge): Still reasonably frequent in moorland, as on Culross Moor (Tulliallan) where it was collected in 1866 (RBG).

C. caryophyllea (Spring Sedge): Here and there in dry grassy places, never in much quantity. Listed from Aberdour in 1866 (RBG), and near Old Whitehill in 1980.

C. curta (White Sedge): A bog species, still common on mosses such as Moss Morran, where it was first mentioned in 1858 (RBG), and in other sites where sphagnum remains.

C. demissa (Common Yellow Sedge): Common on damp acid soil, e.g. by the old reservoir at Lochornie (Cleish Hills).

C. diandra (Lesser Tussock Sedge): One of the first Fife sedges to be noticed, being collected from the Ferry Hills marsh in 1794 (RBG and many subsequent recorders). Probably long extinct there, and perhaps also at Otterston Loch (1836 Young to 1919 Templeman); but happily still at Black Loch, Dunduff, where it was first seen in 1852 (Balfour). Also at Steelend Moss, Saline in 1980 (S. J. Leach). Very rare.

C. *dioica* (Dioecious Sedge): The only West Fife record is from Benarty, just inside the District boundary, in 1980 (S. J. Leach). Very rare.

C. *distans* (Distant Sedge): This coastal species has only one extant site, at Donibristle, where it was observed in 1854 (StA). May still be at Aberdour (1834-71 RBG); but unlikely at Inverkeithing (1831 RBG). Very rare.

C. *disticha* (Brown Sedge): Possibly more frequent than the three known sites indicate. These are Cullalo Reservoir, where West saw it in 1905; Lethan's Den; and just off the road west of Ballingry. Rare.

C. *echinata* (Star Sedge): Common in marshy areas, e.g. near Cowdenbeath in 1848/58 (RBG), probably Moss Morran, where it still grows.

C. *extensa* (Salt-marsh Sedge): Previously on the coast near Aberdour (1820 Boswell to 1858 Balfour); Donibristle (1856 StA); and North Queensferry (1887 RBG); but no records for a century. Extinct.

C. *flacca* (Glaucous Sedge): One of the commonest sedges, in dry, grassy ground, as at Lethan's Den, where it was first noted in 1858 (RBG).

C. *hirta* (Hairy Sedge): Common in long grass, usually in damp spots, as near Culross, where it was first observed in 1866 (RBG).

C. *hostiana* (Tawny Sedge): Occurs sparingly in boggy areas. Still in the Lethan's Den area, 1839 (Campbell)→; Devilla Forest, 1854 (Balfour's "Tulliallan")→; and on Moss Morran; Benarty; etc.

C. *laevigata* (Smooth Sedge): One of the very few Fife stations is in Lethan's Den, which is almost certainly Balfour's "near Dunfermline" record of 1837. Very rare.

C. *lepidocarpa* (Long-stalked Yellow Sedge): Not seen for many years near North Queensferry (1831/47 RBG); but present at Lethan's Den; Roscobie Reservoir; Benarty; Craigencat, Cleish Hills; and Moor Loch (N. F. Stewart). Rare.

C. *limosa* (Mud Sedge): Collected at Otterston Loch between 1825 (RBG) to 1838 (StA), but not later. Found at Benarty in 1980 by S. J. Leach, one of its few extant VC85 stations. Very rare.

C. *magellanica* (Bog Sedge): Gathered from the bog at the foot of Knock Hill (Din Moss) between 1852-74 (RBG); no further Fife record until 1980, when S. J. Leach came across a small colony in the Cleish Hills near the Kinross border in 1980. Very rare.

C. *muricata*, ssp. *lamprocarpa* (Prickly Sedge): Seemingly sporadic in appearance, the only current record being near Torrie House in 1986. Seen in 1836 (Young) at Aberdour and near the station there in 1969 but it subsequently disappeared owing to spraying. Another old site is Muir Dam, Tulliallan (pre-1890 White).

C. *nigra* (Common Sedge): The commonest sedge, still in several of its old sites, e.g. near Loch Gelly, where it was found in 1849 (RBG).

C. *otrubae* (Fox Sedge): Still in most of its seaside stations, including between North Queensferry and Inverkeithing, 1831 (RBG)→; near Kincardine, 1836 (RBG)→; Aberdour, 1863 (B and S)→; etc. Local.

C. *ovalis* (Oval Sedge): Very common in grassy areas, as near Cowdenbeath, where it was noticed in 1858 (RBG).

C. *pallescens* (Pale Sedge): The two old records are from Tulliallan in 1854 (StA), and Dunfermline in 1863 (B and S); the latter may in fact have been Lethan's Den, where it was seen in 1971. Also present by the Black Devon in the Saline Shaw area in 1981. Rare.

C. *panicea* (Carnation Sedge): Common in damp places, as at Roscobie Reservoir.

C. *paniculata* (Tussock Sedge): Seen by the Misses Boswell in 1820 at the west end of Otterston Loch, where West noted it in 1905 "dominating the bog", and which it was still doing 80 years later. Also at Lethan's Den, 1971→; by a pool on Roscobie Hills; plus the odd clump elsewhere in the District. Locally common.

C. *pauciflora* (Few-flowered Sedge): The sole record is from the foot of Knock Hill (Din Moss) in 1852/53 (Balfour; RBG). Extinct.

C. *pendula* (Drooping Sedge): More or less naturalised in Pittencrieff Glen, Dunfermline.

C. *pilulifera* (Pill Sedge): Local in grassy or heathy areas, as near Gartarry, north of Kincardine.

C. *pulicaris* (Flea Sedge): This little plant may yet be detected in damp ground here and there, including at Inverkeithing, 1836 (RBG)→; on Benarty, 1926 (Young)→; on Moss Morran; etc. Rather local.

C. *remota* (Remote Sedge): An "Aberdour" record of 1820 (Boswell) may well be the same as Templeton's 1919 "Donibristle", i.e. in a damp wood near the shore at Dalgety Bay, where John Crichton found it in 1981. Also in Lethan's Den; in Meadowhead Den, at the west end of the Cleish Hills; near Bordie Farm, Tulliallan (N. F. Stewart); and by the Bluther Burn at Valleyfield (N. F. Stewart). Very local.

C. *riparia* (Greater Pond Sedge): Collected from the pond in Tulliallan Castle grounds in 1853 (StA) and still there; probably originally introduced. Very rare (other old records refer to C. *acutiformis*).

C. *rostrata* (Bottle Sedge): Common at the edges of ponds and reservoirs, and in other wet parts. Still in the marsh on the Ferry Hills, where it was collected in 1831 (RBG).

C. *spicata* (Spiked Sedge): The first — and only — Fife record was in 1980 when S. J. Leach discovered a small colony at Charleshill Point, near Braefoot Bay. It is to be hoped that recent developments there have not destroyed the site of this very rare sedge.

C. *sylvatica* (Wood Sedge): Curiously, there are no old records for this graceful sedge, which grows in Lethan's Den; in Valleyfield woods; in Comrie Dean; and east of Torryburn. Rather local, never occurring in quantity.

Festuca pratensis (Meadow Fescue): This species has its few Fife and Kinross localities centred on the Dunduff/Roscobie area, and toward the west end of the Cleish Hills. An old Ferry Hills record of 1835/36 (Robertson; Young) was repeated in 1954 (RBG), but has not been seen there by the writer.

F. gigantea (Giant Fescue): This tall attractive grass increases in frequency in suitable habitats westwards from Torryburn in the south and from Redcraigs/Dunduff in the north. Oddly, there are no old records.

Vulpia myuros (Ratstail Fescue): "Near North Queensferry, on the hill by the road leading to Inverkeithing" stated Greville in 1824; 160 years later it may still be seen, but on the nearby Rosyth branch railway line (with *V. bromoides*). This is one of only two Fife stations.

Desmazeria rigida (Fern Grass): Mentioned from Inverkeithing Parish in 1836 (Robertson), and seen in the area of the town in 1961 (RBG); and at Charleshill Point in 1980 (S. J. Leach). The Charlestown (1835 Robertson) and St Davids (1865/1903 RBG) records may refer to ballast introductions.

D. marina (Darnel Fescue): The only records are old — from North Queensferry (1836 RBG), and Aberdour (1857 RBG); easily overlooked, so could still be extant.

Catabrosa aquatica (Water Whorl-grass): Unfortunately, the only records of this attractive and uncommon grass are all old ones: Inverkeithing/North Queensferry area (1836-58 RBG); near Aberdour (1849 RBG); and Dunfermline (1863 B and S).

Briza media (Quaking Grass): Rather local in undisturbed grassland, as on the Roscobie Hills and Benarty.

Melica uniflora (Wood Melick): This delicate grass may still be admired in three old sites — Lethan's Den, 1834 (Robertson)→; Dunimarle, Culross, 1835 (Robertson)→; and Blair Den, Culross, 1834 (Dewar)→; plus Comrie Dean, 1985 (H. E. Stace)→. Also previously listed from Morton Woods near Aberdour (1834/48 StA; RBG). It should be noted that a close relative, *M. nutans*, was also mentioned from the first three stations, almost certainly in error.

Bromus ramosus (Hairy Brome): Locally common in dens and old woodland, as near Charlestown, where Balfour saw it in 1850; and in Aberdour area, where it was first found in 1820 (Boswell).

Leymus arenarius (Lyme Grass): Although common on the east coast of Fife, this diminishes markedly the further west one goes; the only record is at Port Laing, North Queensferry, in 1967. Its frequent companion, *Ammophila arenaria* (Marram Grass) has not been recorded at all.

Elymus caninus (Bearded Couch): A surprisingly rare plant in VC85, with only one old site in West Fife, near Inverkeithing (*Scottish Geographical Magazine* 1900); and one modern locality, near the mouth of the Bluther Burn, 1984 (N. F. Stewart).

E. farctus (Sand Couch): Rare in sandy places by the sea; in 1967 it was still at Port Laing, where Robertson noticed it in 1835; while N. F. Stewart saw it at St Davids in 1982, where it had been collected in 1869 (RBG).

Avenula pratensis (Meadow Oat): Rather local on the coast, as on the Ferry Hills, where it was first observed by Greville in 1824; also west of Downing Point; and on Hawkcraig (N. F. Stewart) in 1982.

A. pubescens (Hairy Oat): Rather local, chiefly on the coast; mentioned in 1824 from "about North Queensferry" by Greville and seen there 150 years later by O. M. Stewart. Also at Charleshill Point; east of St Davids; and inland at Lethan's Den.

Koeleria macrantha (Crested Hairgrass): In dry grassy areas, local; still on the Ferry Hills, where it was first seen in 1842 (Parnell); and at Donibristle, 1848 (RBG)→; etc.

Trisetum flavescens (Yellow Oat): Still near St Davids, where Balfour listed it in 1856; and at the Ferry Hills; Charleshill Point; Kincardine; and perhaps in one or two other spots.

Calamagrostis epigejos (Bushgrass): In 1886, this was noted at Charlestown, almost certainly having been introduced with ballast. Within 20 years "a large patch" had become established (Evans) but there were no further records until 1979, when it was realised that the grass was widespread on the ash lagoons at Longannet, and present at Culross and Low Valleyfield — and still at Charlestown. Also frequent across the Forth at Grangemouth.

Milium effusum (Wood Millet): Still near Blair Castle, which was probably Robertson's "Culross Woods" station of 1835; and almost certainly in other suitable woods, although not common. Balfour found it in the Tulliallan area in the 1850/60s.

Parapholis strigosa (Sea Hardgrass): In 1871 Tom Drummond collected this from a saltmarsh at Inverkeithing, considering it to be evidently indigenous; four years later he found it "in great profusion" (*BSE*; RBG; and *Journal of Botany* 13, 1875 p380). This is rather extraordinary because (a) there are only a handful of Scottish records, and (b) it seems never to have been reported again. Could it have come in with ship's ballast, like its close relative *P. incurva* did at St Davids in the 1830s?

REFERENCES

B and S = BALFOUR, J. H. and SADLER, J. 1863. Flora of Edinburgh. 2nd edition 1871.

BALFOUR, I. B. 1907. Eighteenth century records of British plants. *Notes of the Royal Botanic Garden Edinburgh* 4, 127-192.

BALFOUR, J. H. 1902. Botanical excursions . . . 1846-1878. *Ibid* 2, 21-497.

BALLANTYNE, G. H. 1970. The Flowering Plants of Kirkcaldy and District. Kirkcaldy Naturalists' Society.

BALLANTYNE, G. H. 1971. Ballast aliens in south Fife, 1820-1919. *Transactions of the Botanical Society of Edinburgh* 41, 125-137.

BALLANTYNE, G. H. 1977. The Flowering Plants of Kinross. 2nd ed. 1985. Scottish Wildlife Trust.

BALLANTYNE, G. H. 1982. Wild Flowers, pp81-104, of The Wildlife and Antiquities of Kirkcaldy District, edited by G. H. Ballantyne. Kirkcaldy Naturalists' Society.

BLAIR, P. 1724. Pharmaco-botanologia. Part II p79.

BOSWELL, E. and M. 1820. List of plants growing in the neighbourhood of Balmuto. Ms.

BSE = Botanical Society of Edinburgh Transactions for the year mentioned.

BUCHANAN, ?. 1880. Hints on the flora of Clackmannanshire and surrounding districts. *Transactions of the Stirling Field and Archaeological Society* 2, 16-25.

CAMPBELL, ?. 1839. Notice of an excursion to the Black Devon . . . June 1839. *Annual Report of the Botanical Society of Edinburgh*, 112-116.

CHALMERS, P. 1844/59. Historical . . . account of Dunfermline. Volume 1, 68-70. Volume 2, 114.

DEWAR, A. 1834-46. Correspondence A. Dewar and J. W. Hooker (in Kew).

DEWAR, A. 1844. Botany (of Dunfermline parish). New Statistical Account 9, 844 (similar list in Chalmers, 1844).

EDINBURGH = Edinburgh Field Naturalists Society Transactions for the year mentioned.

EVANS, W. Annotations to Balfour and Sadler's Flora of Edinburgh, 2nd edition 1871. (Marked copy belonging to Evans covering c1890-1925, now in the author's possession).

FRASER, J. 1903. Alien plants near Edinburgh. *Annals of Scottish Natural History* 13, 112-113.

GLASGOW = Glasgow Natural History Society Proceedings and Transactions for the year mentioned.

GRAHAM, R. 1835. List of plants . . . observed . . . in various excursions from Edinburgh. *Edinburgh New Philosophical Journal* 19, 346-351.

GREVILLE, R. 1824. Flora Edinensis.

HOOKER, J. D. 1821. Flora Scotica.

HOPE, J. 1764/68. See Balfour, I. B. 1907.

LIGHTFOOT, J. 1777. Flora Scotica.

MACKAY, J. 1801. Letters. *Notes of the Royal Botanic Garden Edinburgh* 3, 1903-08, 40-48.

MACMILLAN, H. 1857. Excursions to Castle Campbell and the Saline Hills. *The Phytologist* New Series 2, 258.

MACRITCHIE, W. 1897. Diary of a Tour Through Great Britain in 1795, pp2-3.

MAUGHAN, R. 1809. List of rarer plants observed in the neighbourhood of Edinburgh. *Memoirs of the Wernerian Natural History Society* 1, 215-248.

NSA = New Statistical Account. Volume 9, Fife. Parish accounts for Carnock, 1843; Dunfermline, 1844; and Inverkeithing, 1836; and Volume 10, Perthshire. Parish account for Culross, 1839.

PARNELL, R. 1842. The Grasses of Scotland.

PHYTOLOGIST for the year mentioned.

REID, A. 1886. List of plants . . . in the *Alloa Advertiser* of 6 March 1886, and in the 1903 book Limekilns and Charlestown, 110-112.

ROBERTSON, A. c1835. An old list of "stations of rarer plants ascertained to grow round Inverkeithing and north of the Forth. By A. Robertson". Communicated by Professor Bayley Balfour. *Transactions of the Botanical Society of Edinburgh* 20, 1894, 84-90. (Many of the species listed in the New Statistical Account for Inverkeithing Parish, compiled by Robertson, are included in this account).

TEMPLEMAN, A. 1919. VC85 records. *Report of the Botanical Exchange Club* 5, 616-693 (passim).

WALKER, J. 1808. Essays on Natural History and Rural Economy.

WEST, G. 1910. A further contribution to a comparative study of the . . . flora . . . in Scottish lakes. IV – Area VII (Fife and Kinross). *Proceedings of the Royal Society of Edinburgh* 30, 147-181.

WHITE, F. B. W. 1898. The Flora of Perthshire.

WOODFORDE, J. 1824. A Catalogue of the Indigenous Phenogamic Plants Growing in the Neighbourhood of Edinburgh.

YOUNG, W. 1936. A list of the flowering plants and ferns recorded from Fife and Kinross (VC85). *Transactions of the Botanical Society of Edinburgh* 32, 1-173.

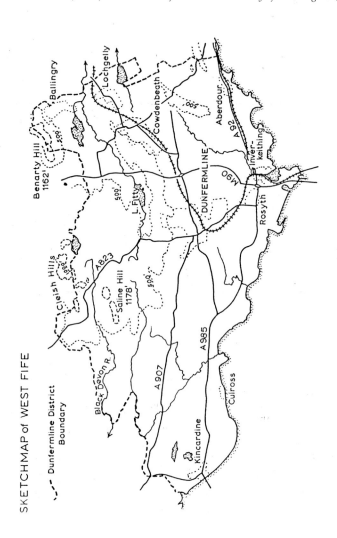

QUEEN MARY AT ALLOA TOWER, 1566

David Angus

It was Sir James Barrie who once observed that when a Scotsman had nothing else to do, he leaned against a wall, put his hands in his pockets and thought about Mary, Queen of Scots.

There is certainly plenty to think about. Nothing about that Royal Lady was unambiguous. And everything about her was — and is — a paradox.

You could, I suppose, call her an Enigma, but she was an Enigma with Variations. Not silent, laconic, cold, uncommunicative, aloof — quite the opposite. She spoke a great deal, wrote a great deal, was frequently indiscreet. Her life was closely observed by friends and enemies — as closely as a Royal personage's life could well be.

Her heart was frequently seen to rule her head. She was voluble, vivacious, extrovert, given to confiding in people; she frequently expressed her own most powerful feelings with sincerity and eloquence. And yet — and yet. . . . The questions remain.

She baffles not only today's historians, scholars, novelists — and yesterday's. She baffled and confused and misled the people of her own day. She had — and has — a baffling effect.

Because of her apparent openness, her indiscretions, her blatant deployment of sexual charm, her transparent manipulations, her detectable lies, her fatal capacity — and preference — for living dangerously, her sheer busy-ness, one is forever tempted to leap to conclusions about her. She seems so obvious — her style is so obvious. Yet of course people leapt — and leap — to their own conclusions, and she leaves them to do that. They leapt, or leap, to multiple, manifold conclusions — which tend to cancel one another out.

And when I turn to the apparently simple matter of her brief visit to Alloa Tower in late July and early August 1566, you will find, as I have done, that none of it is simple and straightforward. Not even that little bit of her life was. Let me list some of the questions that beset us here alone:—

Why did she proceed to Alloa by water, up the Firth and the River Forth from Newhaven, when she had a perfectly good carriage and horses?

With whom did she go? Did the Earl of Bothwell accompany her in place of her estranged husband Darnley?

Or, was Mary accompanied on the river by her illegitimate half-brother, the Earl of Moray, nephew of the Earl of Mar?

Did the Earl of Mar himself go with her? Did her secretary, Maitland of Lethington, recently estranged from her?

We hear that all of these were with her; that one or other, or some of these were with her. We hear that none of these were on the vessel. (I'm inclined to believe the last.)

Who were her companions on the voyage, then? Obviously, the crew of the little vessel. Who were they? George Buchanan, her chief traducer, tells us, with lip-smacking relish, in his *Rerum Scoticarum Historia* — "William and Edmund Blaccader, Edward Robertson and Thomas Dickson, all Bothwell's men and notorious pirates". And he adds "Accompanied by these scoundrels, then, to the astonishment of all good men, she put to sea, attended by not one honest servant".[1] (William Blaccader was later hanged for involvement in Lord Darnley's murder.)

Mary's admirers, of course, point out that the Earl of Bothwell was at this time Lord High Admiral of Scotland, and that that particular crew was licensed to attack and capture pirates anywhere they found them.[2] They also point to Mary's claim that she was accompanied by honest people — in fact by the ladies of her court.[3]

So you have two varying accounts of this little voyage — even if you cut out the Lords I have mentioned. On the one hand we have this skittish queen alone at sea with a bunch of Bothwell's sea-going cut-throats, by day an honorary sailor, skipping up and down rope-ladders and handling cables (we're told),[4] by night up to who knows what below decks.

On the other hand, a pleasant picture emerges of Mary, surrounded by the ladies of her court, sailing in a vessel crewed by eminently respectable seamen, gently and ailingly up the Forth, still convalescent after the birth of Prince James a few weeks before, to spend a safe, quiet few days within the eleven-foot thick walls of Alloa Tower with the eminently respectable Lord and Lady Mar. (Mary had granted him the title a year before).[5]

What were her motives in going to Alloa in any case? Were her reasons lascivious? health-restorative? or political? She needed to get Lethington back in her team. He was in or around Stirling in late July;[6] she might have been angling for him. The Earl of Bradford heard she was to meet Lethington at Alloa on August 2. The two did meet and became reconciled, officially, at Stirling on September 4.[7]

Or was it to get away from someone that she went off to Alloa? Why, after all, did she slip away from Edinburgh Castle on Saturday, July 27,[8] without telling Darnley,[9] to catch a vessel that was obviously waiting for her by secret pre-arrangement?

Those who argue thus certainly have plenty backing for their claim. After Lord Darnley's involvement, four months before, in the murder of her unpopular favourite David Riccio (of whom he had been absurdly jealous), Mary had had little time for him.

As a would-be ruler Darnley was a disaster, idle and indifferent; as a husband he seems to have been a sulky and sullen spoilt brat, who preferred being out 'on the town' with disreputable companions to accompanying his wife; probably unfaithful, possibly homosexual.

Mary's second husband was indeed callous, vain, weak, stupid, foolhardy, and one only wonders how he lived as long as he did in the Scotland of that time. It could only have been Mary's reluctant or indulgent protection that preserved him while he lasted. In any case he was a feeble shuttlecock who eventually, and inevitably, got knocked out of court.

At the time of the Alloa visit Darnley was virtually friendless — he had betrayed the Riccio murderers by escaping from Holyrood with Mary — and was evidently doing his best to re-establish his position as Mary's husband and potential King of Scotland. He was, however, constantly frustrated in both these aims, and in consequence was in a state of continuous boiling resentment, aggravated by personal anxiety. When he heard, belatedly, that she had gone off to Alloa, he promptly followed her — not by water but on horseback, with a train of servants, overland via Stirling Brig.[10] Which brings us to other questions:—

We need scarcely ask why he went? It was precisely in Darnley's character to rush in where he was patently not wanted. In any case, I shall discuss his mood and motives later. But how was he received when he turned up, without invitation or warning, with a train of servants, on Lord Mar's doorstep?

One account has it that Mary welcomed him, that Darnley stayed two days and nights with her at the Tower, that they slept together, and were blissfully, if temporarily, reconciled.[11] Another account cuts it down to one night[12]

None of this coincides with Mary's own account, passed on to us in her *Memoirs*, transcribed by her French secretary Claude Nau during her English captivity. Nor, indeed, with the account given by Buchanan, the mouthpiece of her political and Protestant enemies.

What Nau says is this: "While she was on this excursion (i.e. to Alloa) the King (i.e. Darnley) visited her, making, as it were, a passing call. He spent only a few hours with her, although it had been arranged that they should go back to Edinburgh Castle together".[13] In short, according to Nau, Darnley paid a casual, indeed a flying, visit, got into a huff and did one of his celebrated walking-out acts.

Buchanan? He agrees about the few hours' duration of Darnley's visit, but he sees it all rather differently, as you might expect:

"When the King heard of her unexpected departure, he followed by land as fast as he could, with the hope and purpose of being alone with her, that he might enjoy his conjugal rights. But as if he were an unwelcome intruder upon their pleasures (whoever 'they' were), he was ordered to return whence he came, hardly being allowed time to refresh his servants".[14]

In another version he wrote, Buchanan goes into more suggestive detail: "He (Darnley) was hardly suffered to remain an hour or two, while his horses and servants received food and rest . . . (He was) compelled to take himself off, for fear of more serious injury; and yet she herself passed several days there, if not in princely magnificence, yet in more than princely, or rather unprincely licentiousness".

"At Alloa Tower (he tells us, with bated breath) "she disregarded not only the Majesty of a Queen, but even the modesty of a married woman".[15]

One account says Mary refused even to see her husband, evidently entrenching herself upstairs on the top floor.[16]

You see what I mean. There are a whole series of questions remaining unanswered or rather, variously answered, even about this short sojourn of hers. But enough of questions.

What about some likely answers? Well, we may venture to guess at some, surely.

Why did she go by water? That may well have been the most comfortable way, for a woman not long past a difficult confinement. It may also have been the safest way. With a male heir in existence, many must have seen their Catholic queen as dispensable. On the road she could have been killed, or kidnapped, as Bothwell kidnapped her later on that same road, at Cramond Brig.

Then there was Darnley, the eternal Darnley. Had she gone off by road, we may be sure that the moment he woke up to her departure, he would have leapt on a fast horse. He would certainly have caught her up on the way, and imposed his unwelcome and embarrassing company upon her. She must have been all the more furious when he still turned up at Alloa Tower, but at least there he could be asked firmly to leave. It was Mar's house.

It seems certain that Bothwell, Mar and Moray (pace Holinshed)[17] did not go with her. Had Bothwell gone, you may be quite certain Buchanan would have made the most of it, instead of stopping at dark hints about the sailors on the ship. (The latter, you may be sure, were on their best behaviour, being Bothwell's men.)

As to Mary's motives for going — I imagine they were a combination of several possibilities. She was a new mother, in her mid-twenties, with a duffer for a husband. She was a young and comparatively inexperienced monarch, beset by enemies and plots, inside and outside Scotland.

Therefore, surely, she went off to spend a week or two in a safe castle, consulting with the nearest thing to a father she now had in Scotland. He was also the man who was to protect and rear the child-Prince; one of her chief and most respected counsellors; the Keeper of Edinburgh Castle (as he still was at that point). And, (though neither of them could know this then) he was to rise to be Chancellor of Scotland in the last year of his life, while she languished in an English prison. The Earl of Mar was, and was to be, a major figure in her thinking, and in her life, and in that of her son.

Moreover, Mar was not a roaring rapscallion like Bothwell, an ill-natured numbskull like Darnley, an embittered bastard like his nephew Moray, a foul-mouthed bully (like many of her Lords), a bigoted liar like his friend Buchanan, a moral pillar of salt like John Knox. He may have been dull and safe and solid — his portrait certainly suggests that — but Mary, being none of these, may for once have wished to lean on the dull, the safe, the solid.

How did the first Earl respond to this appeal? We can only guess, but it seems, very well. His first test must have been the sudden, dramatic arrival of Harry, Lord Darnley. Now Darnley could make a very great nuisance of himself. We don't know how many servants he took with him, but I should guess enough to be potentially troublesome. Consider, too, the heated mood in which Darnley must have arrived.

Being a late bedder and late riser, he may have wakened up late (literally) to Mary's flight from Edinburgh. She had left no message, no invitation to follow. She had, in effect, left **him**, abandoned him, deserted him. What did it mean? She was scarcely likely to have fled to the arms of Bothwell — not publicly — but was this a question of the Queen isolating him, leaving him to his own slender resources, among potential enemies, even murderers? He had been isolated enough already while Mary toiled away at sewing together an unlikely Queen's Party that included such disparate elements as Bothwell and Moray. But so long as they (i.e. he and Mary) had slept under the same roof, even if not actually in the same chamber, the fiction of their married life and regnant partnership could be maintained. Now it was a farce, a naked pretence for all to see.

And so, precipitately, he had raced off after her. When he got to Alloa, not having paused to refresh either himself or his servants or horses on the way, he must have been in a desperate mood, ready to rage, reproach, weep, plead — go over the emotional top, one way or another. At heart, what he probably longed for most was a bed within Alloa's four stout walls, an invitation to stay, to renew the Edinburgh Castle situation.

The fact that he came and went — without incident, and pretty quietly and quickly — must I think be something of a tribute to the Earl. I would guess that the sulky hothead was handled with an adroit mixture of consummate courtesy and stern firmness. The Erskines, after all, had had a long history of successfully looking after turbulent young Royal Stuarts. That was why they always got it to do.

On this occasion, Darnley must have been invited to leave (by Mary's orders, of course) almost right away. He did dig his heels in and insist on rest and food for his exhausted servants and horses. Those he got, but evidently that was all he got. After a couple of hours, they were out, and Darnley did not think to come back. Poor Harry, the first and last of Scotland, had to head for Dunfermline and seek a bed for the night.

How long did Mary's visit actually last? Let's try to find an answer to that, too.

In her *Memoirs*, Mary herself placed the visit in early August 1566. In fact she left Edinburgh, as we've seen, on Saturday, July 27th. How long the voyage took we don't know. Not long, if winds and tides were favourable. We know she was in Alloa at least from the 28th,[18] and her stay did spill over into early August. We know she was back in Edinburgh by August 7th,[19] a Wednesday. You could say she had had ten days' break.

But it was not all play. The business of government had to go on, and Mary took that very seriously. During her visit there was at least one meeting of the Privy Council at Alloa; there was an official reception for the French ambassador,[20] and she wrote and despatched three letters of an official nature.[21] Or so the record reads.

It is tantalising not to know what Mary did to relax at Alloa. It was the summer season; she would not have been indoors much through the day. There would have been gardens and policies to walk about in; she would have ridden, or even walked, through the little town, which in those days pressed nearer to the Tower than it does now. And much of the town and the country round about would have been familiar to her from her own childhood, which, in its first six years, was pretty well divided between Stirling and Alloa. That had only been 18 years before. Many of the locals must have had memories of the 'bawbee' princess. How much Mary herself recalled, we cannot tell; perhaps only general impressions.

Nor am I familiar enough with the Mars' — perhaps I should say the Erskines' — domestic arrangements to know what they would have laid on for the Queen in the way of entertainment, indoors or outdoors, e.g. whether she was able to 'play at the gowf', or to practise archery, or to go hunting from the Tower. Certainly Mar was shortly to be hunting with her at Meggetland, in the Borders.[22]

I don't know whether she could dance at night in the Great Hall, or play cards, in what I think must have been a rather sober household. Was there music, song, poetry; flirting, teasing, chat — all the happy trivia in which Mary liked to divest herself of the cares of state? Or was it all pretty dreich and dour? I don't think it could have been quite like that, or she wouldn't have to put up with it for nearly a fortnight.

They would certainly have eaten well. Mar, who was a moderate Protestant in religion — married to a Catholic, forsooth; who was a neutral animal politically,[23] is said to have been chiefly interested in "the pleasures of the table".[24] Lady Antonia Fraser, in another connection, ventures to suggest he suffered from halitosis — bad breath.[25] There could have been a connection!

But we can't tell much by considering the visit alone. Perhaps the best way to study the true relationship between Mary and the Mars is to look and see what happened between them before and after that visit. The watershed in that relationship, as in many of the Queen's relationships in Scotland, came six months later with the violent death by murder of that young man whom the Mars had sent packing from their doors — Henry, Lord Darnley.

The murder occurred in Edinburgh about two in the morning of Monday, 10th of February in the following year. The house in which Darnley was lodged, Kirk o' Field — he had been taken there by the Queen herself from Glasgow while he was ill — was blown up. Darnley, however, was not killed by the explosion. His body — evidently strangled — and that of a male servant were discovered laid out in the snow-covered gardens of the demolished house. People have been arguing about that particular enigma ever since. For very thorough studies of it, I recommend George Malcolm Thomson's book *The Crime of Mary Stuart* and Professor Gordon Donaldson's *The First Trial of Mary, Queen of Scots*.

Henry Stewart, Lord Darnley, was probably one of the most expendable young men who ever lived — a worthless embarrassment to everyone, including his wife — but the manner of his going rocked the Scottish, and indeed the European establishments to their foundations. Mary's name, if not exactly mud at this point, turned a nasty shade of grey.

Did she deserve that? Mary was, perhaps, the least cold-hearted monarch that ever reigned. Even when on bad terms with Darnley (as after Riccio's murder, in which he was blatantly involved) she found kind things to do for him. For instance, soon after the Alloa snub — and perhaps because of it — she presented him with expensive gifts.[26] They went hunting together at Traquair; she tended him during his illness; she was known to have had him in her room overnight at Holyrood on one occasion;[27] she may have slept with him on others;[28] the dead twins she herself said she bore at Loch Leven Castle in 1567 may well have been his, though by that time she was married to Bothwell.

But these instances of kindness were typical, and (for the most part) short-lived lapses on Mary's part. In general, between Riccio's murder and Darnley's own, her second husband had played (to say the least) a peripheral rôle in her life. Very often a humiliating and humiliated rôle. Mary, like most of the Stuarts, was fatally given to playing favourites, and her new and favourite ally, the ambitious and dangerous Bothwell, had loomed larger and larger over this period.

So, of course, Bothwell was now widely suspected of instigating and managing the murder of Darnley, and the besotted Mary was suspected of being art and part. Other lords — though certainly not the upright Mar — had also been involved, but Bothwell and Mary were the main targets of obloquy. Posters appeared mysteriously overnight in public places in Edinburgh, pointing the finger at the Hare and the Mermaid, by which was meant Bothwell and Mary. The man who stuck them up was the Countess of Mar's brother.[29] He was pursued, but not caught.

Bothwell submitted to being tried for the murder in the Canongate Tolbooth, but the Tolbooth was surrounded by his own personal army during the proceedings, and, curiously enough, he was found to be innocent. When I add that Bothwell also happened to be the Sheriff of Edinburgh and in charge of the investigation into Darnley's murder, you may appreciate the truly Gilbertian situation obtaining in that place at that time. Mary, willingly or unwillingly, smiled and approved it all.

But it was an explosive situation that could not go on. If Scotland simply allowed it all to happen, if it too smiled and approved, sooner or later European obloquy would spread to it, and worse could follow. When Bothwell, two months later, proceeded first to kidnap the Queen (perhaps with her collusion) and then, having obtained a swift divorce from his wife, to marry the Queen (certainly with her collusion), that was to add insult to injury. These two madcap adventurers, racing hand-in-hand down the road to ruin, had signed their own sentences of doom.

The two, victims of a kind of *folie à deux*, were virtually isolated in no time. They were almost besieged in Holyrood; they **were** besieged in Borthwick Castle, south of Edinburgh; at Carberry Hill they were forced to separate, and Mary was dragged off to her capital, spat at, vilified, abused and humiliated by her own people. At Langside, after her Loch Leven captivity in the hands of Mar's sister Margaret Douglas (nee Erskine) and Mar's nephew Moray, she was defeated and driven to flee into England and 19 years of captivity.

At Borthwick, Carberry and Langside, Mar was one of the great leaders of the anti-Marian forces. How exactly did all this come about? It will not do to be as summary as this. Let us consider all that the Earl of Mar did, and was, before and after that visit to Alloa. Let us not forget, too, his very formidable Catholic Countess, born the Lady Annabella Murray, sister of the Laird of Tullibardine (the poster-sticker); and Mar's equally formidable sister, Margaret whom I've just mentioned, now a pillar of Protestant respectability and *chatelaine* of Loch Leven Castle, but once a King's mistress and the model for Sir David Lyndesay's "Dame Sensualitie".

But let me concentrate on the Erskine I've dared to call dull — John, first Earl of Mar (Mary had made him that, don't forget, in 1565). Dull he may have been, with his hangdog looks and his hangdog beard, but he was tough and shrewd too, and, as we'll see, he could handle Mary as firmly, as diplomatically and as expertly as he could Darnley.

Let us begin with the happier times. Mar's traditional rôle was as Keeper or Governor of Edinburgh Castle. He fulfilled this rôle with total loyalty to the Crown. In 1560 he had held that fortress for Mary's mother, Mary of Guise, when an English Protestant army was fighting with her French forces around Edinburgh and elsewhere.

Five years later, he had held it for Mary, when Moray and other lords, disappointed by Mary's marriage to the Catholic Darnley, had whipped up a Protestant rebellion of sorts. In March 1566, Mary, about to escape from Holyrood after Riccio's murder, sent a message to Mar at the Castle asurring him of her coming escape and return to power, and insisting he keep the Castle for her meantime — which he duly did.[30]

Her visit to Alloa four months later confirms that she still regarded him, if not as an ally, then certainly as a dependable servant of the Crown — the man most likely to preserve her son from ill. And there was more to it than that. James was not only sole heir to the Scottish throne. He had, through his father as well as his mother, an unimpeachable claim to the English throne, and therefore to what was to become the British throne. Elizabeth was ageing; she had and she would have no children. James, if he lived, would make it certain that Mary's dearest wish — to see a Stuart rule Britain — was realised.

Soon after the visit to Alloa, Mary (as I've mentioned) went hunting with Mar and other lords at Meggetland in Peeblesshire. It was during her return thence to Edinburgh (by her own account) that she finally decided that the baby prince should be transferred to Stirling Castle and the Mar's care. And so he was, under armed guard of 500 harquebusiers, and accompanied by his mother.[31]

On December 17 came the sumptuous baptismal ceremonies and celebrations at Stirling. Bothwell played a leading rôle while Darnley, for the most part, sulked in a house at the foot of Broad Street, where they now serve coffee. Bothwell, who in fact received excessive favours from Mary at this sensitive time, was lodged in the northern part of the Great Hall; and the gossips later said that the little bridge between the Palace and the Hall, which still exists, was erected at this time by Mary's orders, to allow her to slip over clandestinely to Bothwell's bed.[32]

Bothwell, in fact, seemed nervous of someone else coming to his bed to tickle him in a rather different way. He had guards round it all night.[33] Perhaps he feared Darnley, or some agent of Darnley's, might come at him with a dagger; perhaps he realised how unpopular he was becoming with the other Lords. In any case, he actually sent outside the castle for reinforcements. But when a body of 50 harquebusiers turned up at the castle gate, claiming that Bothwell had summoned them there to protect him, Mar summarily refused them entry.[34] Mar was already wary of Bothwell, and perhaps of Mary, and his instincts, as time was to show, were correct.

In January 1567 the Prince did in fact vanish from Stirling Castle, but only because he had been taken by his mother, obviously with Mar's consent. It was claimed that Darnley had designs on the Prince — not on his life (unless he still thought the child was Riccio's), but probably seeing the child as a pawn leading to power and acceptance for himself, and denigration and dismissal for Mary and Bothwell.[35]

It doesn't sound likely. True, Lady Mar did have family connections with Darnley, but Darnley himself was at that time very ill in Glasgow, suffering from a venereal disease. It seems more likely that Bothwell was behind the move; we'll see how he used it later to his own advantage against Mar in a moment. But at least the child was safe enough in its mother's care.

Mar must have grown a great deal uneasier about the matter when he heard, early in February, of Darnley's murder. Rumours of Mary's enslavement to Bothwell would seem to have been confirmed; we may be sure that one of Mar's chief concerns, from then on, would be to get Prince James back into Stirling Castle. Clearly if Bothwell was guilty, Bothwell would have a prime motive for getting rid of James permanently, lest he grew up to revenge his father. (Also, Bothwell fully intended to marry the Queen and father his own princes).

On the 20th of next month (March) Mar at last succeeded in recovering the Prince; and he never let go of James again in his own lifetime, which ended when James was seven. Yes, Mar got the Prince back, but at a price; which was that he had to give up the Governorship of Edinburgh Castle, and accept Stirling instead. We have seen what a powerful strategic fortress Edinburgh Castle was in Mar's hand — and don't forget it contained the Scottish treasury at that time too. Bothwell was determined to pass it on into hands friendlier to himself. Reluctantly, to get hold of the Prince, Mar had to capitulate and give up that Governorship. When he did so Mary (Buchanan tells us) tried to go back on her side of the bargain. And then she tried to have James handed over at Linlithgow, a half-way house where he might easily have been snatched. Certainly Mar suspected some chicanery, and insisted that James be delivered into the Castle of Stirling itself. And so he was.[36]

A month later Mary herself came there, allegedly merely to see James. Mar now distrusted her and during her visit (we are told) made absolutely certain that the child was never out of his sight. Mary retired, having seen her son (though she knew it not then) for the last time. On the way out of Stirling she fell ill (with fury and frustration, her enemies said), but she did reach Linlithgow that night.[37]

It is worth adding at this point that Edinburgh Castle did Bothwell no good at all. The first new appointee as Governor, Sir James Cockburn, turned two of the Castle guns on Bothwell as he rode under the Castle with the kidnapped Queen,[38] and his replacement, the villainous Sir James Balfour (implicated in Darnley's murder), changed sides when he saw the way the wind was blowing.[39] In the event, Mar got the best of the bargain.

Next month, early in May 1567, with Mary kidnapped and in Bothwell's power, Mar had to go one step further and act against his Queen. Annabella's brother Tullibardine and the Earl of Home were the first to come out.[40] They called for a coalition to punish Bothwell for Darnley's murder, get the Queen away from him, divorced, restored as a free monarch, and so on.[41]

Mar came in on Tullibardine's coat-tails, but Mary suspected another instigator. In the *Memoirs* Nau wrote: "To a certain extent the Countess of Mar was the cause, a malevolent woman and full of the spirit of revenge".[42] We must not forget Annabella's family connections with Darnley — and they were both Catholics. Bothwell was a Protestant. It's interesting, but not surprising, that Annabella was just as unpopular with Protestants as she was later with Mary. Knox called her "a Jezebel" and "a sweet morsel for the Devil's mouth". Others said she was "wise and sharp".[43]

In any case, Mar and other moderates planning action, gathered at Stirling Castle. Elsewhere there were the less moderate, whom Bothwell had forced into approving his plan to marry Mary. These now were plotting to dispense with Mary as well as Bothwell, and to rule through the baby Prince. Mar was not yet in sympathy with these.

To get themselves into the right mood at Stirling Castle, Mar and his moderates had a company of boy actors put on a drama about the Murder of Darnley and the Fate of Bothwell. There was a good deal of wishful thinking in all this, and the unfortunate lad chosen to play Bothwell barely survived his mock hanging at the end of the play.[44]

But play soon turned to reality. Mar, along with Argyll, Atholl and Morton, rode at the head of an army in pursuit of Mary, now married to Bothwell. Argyll was the doubtful factor — his wife, Mary's half-sister, had been with Mary when Riccio was murdered. He was said to have betrayed the moderates' plans. There had been, for instance, a plan to surround Mary and Bothwell in Holyrood. They escaped in time, and hied them to Borthwick. There they were besieged, though Mar was rather late on the scene, but Bothwell and Mary effected escapes, on separate nights, Bothwell dressed as a woman (!) and Mary disguised as a page. They met up in due course, and got away to Dunbar. At last, a confrontation of sorts occurred at Carberry Hill, near Musselburgh. Mary's army wouldn't fight — indeed the only man there who did want to fight was Bothwell — he wished to take on Mar and the other Lords successively in single combat. It was typical, futile Bothwell swagger. He had no takers. Mary bargained; Bothwell was allowed to flee, she gave herself up. She never saw him again.

In his absence, Bothwell's effects were searched, and the infamous Silver Casket came to light, full (it was alleged) of incriminating letters and poems written by Mary to Bothwell. Mar was among those who inspected the contents. Needless to say, the originals vanished very quickly; the so-called transcripts are of doubtful authenticity. Many of the originals seem to have been written by Anna Throndsen, a Norwegian lady and one of Bothwell's cast-off mistresses, but the contents, once copied out, edited and added to, could be twisted to incriminate Mary — and indeed they helped do that.

By July 25, 1567, about a month after Carberry, Mar's moderation had evidently grown less moderate. Perhaps the combined voices of his Countess and his sister Margaret at Loch Leven overwhelmed him. In any case, he gave his tacit consent when some of the more brutal Lords physically forced Mary, at Loch Leven, to abdicate her throne in favour of her son. Mar, naturally, was named as one of the guardians of the Prince and, in effect, the little James remained in his care. Moray was to be Regent.

Then came the episode of Mary's romantic escape from Loch Leven on May 2, 1568. She was taken up by the powerful faction of the Hamiltons in the west and found herself once more at the head of an army. They aimed to take Dumbarton Castle, but were waylaid at Langside by Moray's hastily assembled army, and soundly defeated. Mar, as we have seen, was on the winning side, even though Bothwell was by now safely out of the way in a Scandinavian prison (where in fact he had been landed by Anna Throndsen and her vengeful family.) Mar's attitude had gone on hardening.

Meanwhile, Mary fled to England. Elizabeth was her cousin and fellow Queen — Mary liked to call her 'sister' — and the two had kept up a wary correspondence and a diplomatic friendship over the years. Now Mary must have hoped it all meant something. She may even have had an idea that Elizabeth, in the interest of the Divine Right of Queens, might reinstate her on the Scottish throne.

But Elizabeth was no fool. She knew all about Mary's fatal charm; knew that beneath, there was a will of iron, and a strong ambition to replace her on her own throne. She knew there were thousands of English Catholics ready and willing to see Mary take her place; she saw that Mary could use, or be used by, powerful Catholic allies in Europe. Also, Mary was still young — 26 — still beautiful, still a desirable marriage-morsel for a host of ambitious Lords, with the marriage to Bothwell annulled. Mary, in short, was a walking, talking time-bomb, so far as Elizabeth was concerned.

So, Elizabeth kept her at arms-length; refused to meet her; and kept her under lock and key in the Midlands, under the watchful eyes of the Earl and Countess of Shrewsbury.

But Mar is more my subject than Mary. Mar, don't forget, still had the young King in his care, and much thought revolved round that fact now. What was to become of young James, now virtually motherless as well as fatherless, and in the hands, effectively, of his mother's enemies?

In fact, all that happened to him — and it was bad enough — was that from 1569, when he was four, the Countess of Mar and his tutor (George Buchanan, who else?) combined to din into the little boy's head an absolute detestation of his mother, and of all things Catholic. He had a grim, loveless education, and spent the rest of his life — and he lived to be 60 — trying to recover from it.[45]

But with the Protestants and the pro-English party cock-a-hoop in Scotland, it was natural that lurid rumours should circulate about what they intended for James. When Mary, down in Castle Bolton, heard these rumours, she was either alarmed by them or (if Gordon Donaldson is correct), she decided to fan them for reasons of propaganda.

All this began late in 1569. On December 17 Mary wrote to Mar from her English prison to warn him, in her son's interests. Her story was that her 'rebels' (and she diplomatically did not include Mar in that number) were practising secretly to deliver James to the English, along with the key castles of Edinburgh, Stirling and Dumbarton. Moray — still the Regent — was to be legitimated so that, if anything happened to James, he could reign as a puppet king under the English, and so on.

We don't know what Mar made of all this, but the English Government realised all too well the effect such rumours could have in Scotland. The last thing they wanted was a Scottish invasion, or a Scottish plot, to free Mary, founded on a tide of patriotic, anti-English feeling. So they issued a public denial of all such rumours, and Queen Elizabeth herself sat down to write a personal letter of reassurance to the Earl and Countess of Mar.[46]

Mar, we see, was at the centre of things — in charge of a King, and courted by two Queens. Little wonder he was appointed Chancellor (virtually a King himself) in 1571. Little wonder he began to build his own palace, at the head of Broad Street in Stirling, glowering down to where another 'soi-disant' King had, five years before, glowered up jealously at the seat of power.

In 1572, in September and October, in the wake of the terrible French Massacre of the Huguenots on St. Bartholomew's Eve, Elizabeth toyed with the idea of returning Mary to Scotland, in the hope that anti-Catholic feeling, raised to a new pitch, would carry her off. Eric Linklater, in his book *The Royal House of Scotland*, quotes a lurid yarn that Elizabeth was prepared to do this, provided that Mar (the Chancellor) and Morton (next in line for the Chancellorship) would agree, for a price, to execute Mary. Linklater adds that Morton's price was too high. He doesn't mention Mar's reaction, though he implies he accepted.[47]

My guess is that Mar was asked first and said 'No', but because by now he was old, ill and dying, they tried it on Morton who said 'Yes, but only if . . .' At any rate, Elizabeth, whose heart was not in it, withdrew the offer.[48]

Mar's hour of glory, in any case, did not last long. He died on October 28, 1572; his palace was never finished, and in due course became a workhouse for Stirling's poor — Mar's Wark.

But in his day he triumphantly fulfilled the trust assigned to him on that visit in the summer of '66. He fulfilled it, even in the teeth of the Royal lady who gave it to him. He, and Alloa Tower, stood firm. It is notable that Mary never appears to have written or spoken against him. Perhaps she realised, in her heart of hearts, that all her dynastic hopes for the Stuarts rested — and rested with perfect safety — upon his shoulders.

At the end, interestingly, even the Jesuit priests in Scotland had a word of sympathy for Mar. In 1594 they sent a report on the state of Scotland to Pope Clement, in which one sentence runs: "Although he (Mar) also enjoyed the favour of the Queen of England, yet he was so harassed by the adverse party (presumably Queen Mary's supporters) that he could have peace nowhere, and died in a short time, worn out by trouble and vexation".[48]

As for the end of Mary, let me quote the final two sentences of *The Queen's Maries* by the Victorian novelist Whyte Melville. They paint Mary as she would *like* to have been painted:

"Yet still the stately flower bloomed on, fair and fragrant under the pure air of heaven, fair and fragrant in the close confinement and the darkened daylight of a prison-house . . . But the storm was brewing the while low down in the southern sky; the storm that was about to gather so dark and pitiless, to burst at last in its fury over the Queen of the Roses and lay that lovely head upon the cold earth, beautiful and majestic even in the pale agony of death".[50]

And on that valedictory note, it may be as well to draw the curtain, or close the book, on the Royal Guest at Alloa Tower in 1566.

NOTES/REFERENCES

1. George Buchanan: *The Tyrannous Reign of Mary Stewart*. Translated and edited by W. A. Gatherer, E.U.P. 1958, p.105.
2. Ibid, p.105n.
3. Claude Nau: *The History of Mary Stewart*, edited with historical preface by Rev. Joseph Stevenson, S.J. Edinburgh 1883, p.29.
4. D. Hay Fleming: *Mary, Queen of Scots*, London 1898, p.410 (Note 41 to Chap. XI).
5. E. K. Roy, K. J. H. Mackay and L. Corbett: *Alloa Tower*, Alloa 1987, p.8.
6. Buchanan, ibid, p.105n.
7. Fleming, ibid, p.413. (Note 55 to Chap. XI).
8. Roy, Mackay, Corbett, ibid, p.9.
9. Fleming, ibid, p.136.
10. Buchanan, ibid, p.106n.
11. Fleming, ibid, p.411 (Note 43 to Chap. XI).
12. Roy, Mackay, Corbett, ibid, p.9.
13. Nau, ibid, p.29.
14. Buchanan, ibid, p.106.
15. Ibid, p.167.
16. Roy, Mackay, Corbett, ibid, p.9.
17. Buchanan, ibid, p.105n.
18. Fleming, ibid, p.411 (Note 43 to Chap. XI). Also p.538 (Itinerary).
19. Ibid, p.538 (Itinerary).
20. R. Gore-Brown: *Lord Bothwell*, London 1937, p.256.
21. Fleming, ibid, p.538 (Itinerary).
22. Ibid, p.137.
23. Gore-Brown, ibid, p.90.
24. Ibid, p.134.
25. Antonia Fraser: *Mary, Queen of Scots*, London (Panther), 1970, pp.470-1.
26. Gore-Brown, ibid, p.256; Donaldson, ibid, p.149.
27. Donaldson, ibid, p.149.
28. Fraser, ibid, p.327.
29. Ibid, p.372.
30. Nau, ibid, p.10.
31. Ibid, p.30.
32. Donaldson, ibid, pp.157-8.
33. Ibid, p.158.
34. Ibid, p.158.
35. Ibid, p.159.
36. Buchanan, ibid, p.122 and n.
37. Ibid, p.127 and n.
38. Gore-Brown, ibid, p.364.
39. Ibid, pp.380-1; Fraser, ibid, p.392.
40. Fraser, ibid, p.391.
41. Fleming, ibid, p.463 (Note 25 to Chap. XIII).
42. Nau, ibid, p.41.
43. Gore-Brown, ibid, p.255.
44. Ibid, p.362.

45. Fraser, ibid, p.537.
46. Donaldson, ibid, pp.206-7.
47. E. Linklater: *The Royal House of Scotland*. (London 1970) p.131.
48. Donaldson, ibid, p.222.
49. Nau, ibid, p.133 (Appendix 1).
50. G. J. Whyte Melville: *The Queen's Maries* (London 1862). p.475.

Editorial Notes — Forthcoming

The 16th Man and the Landscape symposium will be on Saturday 17th November at Stirling University. The theme is Loch Lomond with general and lively reviewing of its environment, past, present, and future as Scotland's first National Park. Like the Forth Estuary one last year there will be displays by numerous organisations and an 'introductory' cruise. Programme presenters are — Joy Tivy, Tom Weir, John Mitchell, Roger Tippett and Nicolas Pennington. The Loch Lomond Research Station is approaching its 25th year and a celebratory symposium is planned for 1992 by Glasgow and Stirling Universities. Dr Tippet its Director has arranged with the Regional Park Authority now for a reprint of the *Natural History of Loch Lomond*. A future revision of this may be the *Guide* for the coming National Park.

The Ochil Hills — an introductory booklet with selected walks intended for December 1989 has been delayed but we hope to have it out this summer.

Some papers in hand or in progress which may form volume 13 (late summer) and into 14, include — Climate Report 1989; Moorland Birds; Spring Migrants; Enclosures — a Farmer's View; Dickens at Bridge of Allan; Rock Art of Menteith; Early Gravestones at Holy Rude; Excavations at Airth; Smith of the Museum; Birds of the Devon; The Forth Estuary; Bird Report 1989; Charting of Scottish Lochs; Charles Rogers 1825-90.

THE RISE AND DECLINE OF THE COAL AND RAILWAY INDUSTRIES OF CLACKMANNANSHIRE

B. J. Elliott

In 1990 no passenger trains moved within the county of Clackmannan and only one daily freight train uses its remaining few kilometres of single track between Stirling, Cambus and Menstrie. The railway age in Scotland's smallest county lasted, for all practical purposes, a little over a century. The coal industry, still in operation today, has lasted much longer — at least 400 years. Both coal and rail reached their zenith just before the First World War.

The first stretch of railway line, between Alloa and Dunfermline, was opened in August 1850. This was relatively late in the railway era, a quarter of a century after the first and famous Stockton-Darlington line. The explanation for this delay can be found most probably in the county's proximity to the Forth. For centuries sailing ships constantly plied the river as far as Stirling trading with Germany, France and the Low Countries. Steamboats arrived in 1813 and by 1840 70-ton vessels made regular journeys between Stirling and Newhaven (Leith) carrying passengers at 'exceedingly low fares'.

Once the civil engineers and the navvies of the railway companies entered the county they remained busy on-and-off for the next 45 years. The first line in 1850 belonged to the Stirling and Dunfermline Railway Company but it was two years later before the former town was reached. By this time the Company had also opened (3 June 1851) its branch line from Alloa to Tillicoultry for the transportation of coal. This short stretch of line soon became part of a more grandiose plan to provide an alternative route between Stirling and North-east Scotland to the Scottish Central Railway Company's Stirling-Perth line through Dunblane which opened in 1848. Ten years later the Devon Valley Railway Company had secured powers to link Tillicoultry to what later became Kinross Junction on the Edinburgh to Perth line (following the opening of the Forth Bridge in 1890). Building began in 1860 and on 1 August 1863 the eastern end as far as Rumbling Bridge was opened. Almost six years later (3 May 1869) the Tillicoultry-Dollar section was opened. But the final stretch Dollar to Rumbling Bridge was beset with civil engineering problems which included the construction of 17 bridges and viaducts before it was opened on 1 May 1871.

Meanwhile on 3 June 1863 the Alva Railway Company had opened a single track line just west of Cambus station on the line from Alloa to Stirling. It was hoped to link Alva and Tillicoultry providing a more direct route to Stirling than through Alloa but it proved impossible to get rights of way on this stretch.

All these small companies and indeed all the railways in the county with one exception were eventually incorporated into the North British Railway. The NBR gained an unenviable reputation for high costs, low dividends and inefficiency, never more so than when its ill-fated Tay Bridge collapsed in 1879. The exception to the NBR's dominance in the county was the Alloa Railway Company. This consisted of a single line leaving the South Alloa branch of the Caledonian Railway at Dunmore Moss. It crossed the Forth by a swing bridge, opened in 1885, by which time it had been taken over by the Caledonian. The line entered Alloa through a goods station in Glasshouse Loan in the industrial part of the town. The NBR then put in a connecting line just west of Grange signal box to this new line giving it entry into Alloa station. This allowed both companies to run passenger trains between Alloa and Larbert with connections to Edinburgh and Glasgow. The NBR, however, resisted all attempts by the Caledonian to use this line to gain access to the lucrative coal trade of Clackmannan and Fife. Neither did anything emerge from various attempts to merge the two companies. When large scale mergers came, in 1923, the NBR became part of the LNER and the Caledonian joined the LMSR.

Meanwhile the last line in the county between Alloa and Kincardine, another NBR venture, was initially for freight only in 1893, but in 1906 was opened for passengers, simultaneously with its extension to Dunfermline along the north bank of the Forth.

By 1910 Clackmannanshire's railways were a tiny fraction of the 23,387 route miles (37,400 kms) of the UK network into which £1.3 billion of capital had been poured since 1825. This sum included over £70 million each for the NBR and Caledonian. By 1910 the NBR owned 1352 route miles (2180 kms) and the Caledonian 1074 miles (1718 kms).

Railways completely dominated British inland transport by this time. 23,000 steam locomotives hauled 52,000 passenger carriages and 750,000 freight waggons over a total distance exceeding 400 million miles annually. A workforce of 609,000 men and women, almost 50,000 in Scotland, and paid an average of £1.15p per week for up to 72 hours work, earned for the Railway Companies a gross income of £114 million in 1910. Of this total £47 million (equal to at least £1.5 billion in 1990) was gross profit, of which the share of the NBR and Caledonian was around £2 million each. Railways, therefore, by reason of their dominant position in inland transport were immensely profitable but, through overcapitalisation were an unexciting, although for the time being, safe investment.

The Census of Population in 1911 showed that in Clackmannanshire there lived 285 men and one woman employed by the railway industry. These were 57 officials and clerks, 45 ticket collectors and porters, 34 engine drivers, stokers and cleaners, 18 guards, 36 signalmen, 66 platelayers and gangers, 26 labourers and three pointsmen and crossing keepers, the solitary woman employee being one of the latter. This total was dwarfed by the 1322 men and two women living in the country who earned a living in the coalmining industry. This statistic indicates clearly that it was the coal wealth of Clackmannanshire, well known as early as 1600 which had been the major motivation for the construction of railways in the county. By 1790 production had exceeded 100,000 tons per annum. Two mines in Alloa employing over 500 persons, of whom a majority were women, produced almost half this total. There were another three in the parish of Clackmannan producing a further third and the remaining 25,000 tons came from Dollar and Tillicoultry. A primitive tramway had been constructed through Sauchie to the waterfront at Alloa about 1766 to move these minerals.

The demands of an industrialising and urbanising society in the 19th century brought about an enormous expansion of Scottish coal production. From around two million tons in 1800 it rose to six million in 1850 then soared to its highest ever production of 42 million tons in 1913. This was part of a total UK production of 287 million, dug by more than one million miners in 3300 collieries. A third of this UK production was exported so that Alloa was a modestly expanding port during the 19th century entering and clearing a total of 170,000 tons of cargo by 1913. Not surprisingly freight traffic and especially coal on the UK rail network was of immense importance. In 1910 rail freight totalled over 500 million tons earning £61 million or almost 50 per cent of the railways gross revenue.

Passenger traffic on the UK network had become extremely important also with 1910 receipts from 1.3 billion passengers totalling £53 million equal to 43 per cent of gross revenue. The remaining 7 per cent came from hotels and shipping. As there were no longer any 2nd class seats on Scottish trains by 1910 it was the humble 3rd class passenger paying 0.89d (½p) per mile, and spending seven times as much in total on rail tickets as 1st class passengers (2.35d per mile), who filled the coffers of the railway companies. Undoubtedly it was largely 3rd class passengers who filled the seats on the 57 trains leaving Alloa station each week day between 7.05 am and 10.21 pm in April 1910. A study of the departure timetable (Appendix) shows that Alloa also had its own mini rush-hours with ten of these trains leaving between 7.58 am and 9.00 am and a further 11 in the evening between 5.21 and 6.19 pm. Clearly the passenger train in the small industrial or commercial towns of this period filled exactly the same role as the motorbus today although without the competition of the private car. Neither were the trains of this era much faster than buses today. The 9.00 am Alloa to Ladybank stopping at 12 stations en route took 90 minutes to cover 32 miles. In fact only one mainline train in the UK at this time exceeded an average speed of 60 mph over a significant stretch. The majority of passenger trains leaving Alloa covered short, and no doubt uneconomic journeys. Assuming quite reasonably that all the freight trains moved within the same hours as the passenger trains, the whole rail system within the county closed down for nearly nine hours out of every 24 (and much longer on Sundays), effecting the maximum savings on wages.

By 1923 and the creation of Britain's 'Big Four' companies, railways had already passed their peak. The first closure, the passenger station at Clackmannan Road had already taken place in 1921, a victim of the rapidly expanding motorbus services. The coal industry was in even deeper crisis. Like the railway system it had been taken over by the government in 1914 but as prices tumbled it was handed back to its private owners in 1921. Wage cuts precipitated a major strike, a forerunner to the disastrous confrontation of 1926. The long depression of the coal industry reduced the level of economic activity and income in Clackmannanshire. By the late 1930s there was some revival in the demand for coal and the seven collieries in the county were producing approximately 500,000 tons annually with total reserves estimated at 62 million tons.

However the combined effects of the economic depression and the growing competition from road transport had begun to eat into the profits of the railways. One result had been the withdrawal of the passenger service between Alloa, Kincardine and Dunfermline on 1 July 1930 followed a month later by the closure of the passenger stations at Sauchie and Forest Mill. These closures were but a small fraction of a much larger series at this time, mainly in the old industrial areas and coalfields of Britain.

After another even more remorseless wartime battering the British Rail system was nationalised (1 January 1948) one year after the nationalisation of the coal industry.

At the time of nationalisation nine National Coal Board collieries were in operation in the county and one, Devon Mine, privately owned. The NCB operations were Brucefield (opened 1905), Craigrie (reopened 1942), Devon (1850), Dollar (1943 — partly in Perthshire), King O'Muirs No. 1 (1938), Melloch (1850), Meta Pit (1923), Meta Mine (1946) and Tillicoultry (1876). Employment in coalmining in Clackmannanshire had actually increased 30 per cent between 1911 and 1951. The Census of the latter year indicated that 1724 men and women resident in the county earned their living from the coal industry. It is possible of course that some worked outwith the county. However the high level of economic activity in post-war Britain, the then absence of rival indigeneous fuels and the expansion of the mining operations in the county (there were seven openings between 1942-52 against three closures of collieries) would all have indicated an optimistic future for the industry.

Employment by British Railways in Clackmannanshire as shown by the 1951 Census of Scotland returns had declined by 38 per cent since 1911 to a figure of 173 men and four women. There were 12 officials,

28 locomotive drivers, 21 firemen, four locomotive shedmen, 14 guards, 33 signalmen, 16 shunters, pointsmen and crossing keepers, two ticket collectors, 41 porters and three others.

By contrast employment in the road haulage and road passenger transport industry amongst residents of the county numbered 526 men and 56 women or more than **three** times the number of railway employees.

Despite the evergrowing competition of road transport British Railways remained profitable for a few years after nationalisation. But burdened by debt, attacked by road competition and faced with the need for massive capital investment, the whole rail network, like that in virtually every other country, came quickly to rely on government subsidies.

Inevitably the price of government support was closure of uneconomic lines although within the county only one service was withdrawn in the 1950s. This was the Cambus-Alva branch line on 30 October 1954. A glance at the map shows the unviability of this line which was twice the distance by rail from Alva to Alloa than it was by road and two miles further to Stirling by rail involving also a change of trains at Cambus. The line between Alva and Menstrie was lifted.

The three remaining passenger closures in the county followed the 1963 report on the reshaping of British Railways by Lord Beeching who had been commissioned to staunch the rising losses of British Rail. The Devon Valley line from Alloa to Dollar was closed to passengers on 15 June 1964 and from Dollar to Kinross to all services. The track between Alloa and Dollar was finally closed and dismantled after the closure of Dollar mine in 1973. The Alloa bridge route to Larbert was closed on 29 January 1968 and the Stirling-Alloa-Dunfermline service eight months later on 7 October.

The optimism about the Clackmannanshire coal industry was also misplaced. Between 1948 and 1987 14 collieries belonging to the NCB (now British Coal) were closed. These were variously the result of exhaustion, unprofitability and geological and other technical problems. The Scottish coal industry generally was damaged by competition from nuclear, hydro-electric and oil-fired generation of electricity, in addition to North Sea gas.

The colliery closures in Clackmannanshire were Brucefield (1962), Craigrie (1952), Devon (1960), Dollar (1973), Forthbank (1958), Glenochil (1962), Harviestoun (1961), King O'Muirs No. 1 (1954) and No. 2 (1957), Melloch (1948), Meta Pit (1948), Meta Mine (1959), Tillicoultry No. 1 (1948) and No. 2 (1959). Additionally four privately owned mines have closed. Gartmorn (opened 1962, closed 1986), Gartenkeir (1967-1968), Grasmainstoun (1971-1982) and Devon Mine (1933-1987). By the end of 1987 deep mining operations were in progress within the boundaries of Clackmannanshire only at Castlebridge and Solsgirth and at a private drift mine, under licence at Harviestoun. In addition a small number of open cast operations, again under licence from British Coal were in operation.

None of this coal was being moved out of the county by rail by the end of 1987. Within the county freight traffic has been reduced to one solitary trainload of molasses, originating from East Anglia or imported through Greenock, which is delivered each morning to Glenochil distillery and leaves empty in the afternoon. Additionally sporadic deliveries of grain are made to Cambus distillery and carbon dioxide in tanker waggons is hauled out. In 1987 Scotrail considered building a turntable at Cambus and dismantling the track to Alloa. However, local pressures, including the District Council, to reinstate passenger services from Alloa have been supported by a consultant's report and subsequently by the Regional Council. In early 1990 the track is still there but no final decision about the future has yet been made.

References and Sources

Census of Scotland 1911 vol. 2 (1913) and 1951 vol. 4 (1956).
The Statistical Account of Scotland, Stirling and Clackmannan First, 1790 volume IX; New, 1845 volume VIII; Third, 1966.
Local papers — *Alloa Advertiser, Stirling Journal* and *Stirling Observer.*
Bradshaws Railway Guide April 1910 Reprint, David and Charles 1968.
Brown, William C., Clackmannanshire, A Guide to Historical Sources, Forth Natural Historian, 1980.
Bruce William Scott, The Railways of Fife. Melvin Press, 1981.
Daniels, G. and Dench, L. A., Passengers No More. Shepperton, 1974.
Morris, David B., Early navigation of the Forth, *Transactions of the Stirling Natural History and Archaeological Society* 1919-1920.
Nef, John U., Rise of the British Coal Industry, 2 vols. 1932.
Pratt, Edwin, A History of Inland Transport and Communication, 1912.
Thomas, John, North British Railway, 2 vols. David and Charles. 1969 and 1975.
Whittakers Almanac, 1914.

Acknowledgement

I am indebted for personal communications to David Clayton, Freightrail, Scotrail Glasgow; and John T. Mackie, Head of Technical Services, British Coal, Scottish Area, Edinburgh.

Appendix

The Departures Timetable at Alloa Station, April 1910
(All NBR except (Cal.) = Caledonian. S = Saturdays only)

AM

7.05 (Cal.)	Throsk Platform (7.09), Airth (7.18), Larbert (7.25).
58	Tillicoultry (8.06), Dollar (8.13), Rumbling Bridge (8.23), Kinross Junction (8.41), Perth (9.20).
8.00	Cambus (8.05), Menstrie and Glenochil (8.09), Alva (8.13).
10	Clackmannan and Kennet (8.16), Kilbagie (8.21), Kincardine (8.25).
15	Cambus (8.20), Causewayhead (8.28), Stirling (8.31), Larbert (8.38), Castle Cary (8.49), Dullatur (8.55), Croy (8.59), Cowlairs (9.18), Glasgow (9.24).
18	Clackmannan Road (8.23), Forest Mill (8.27), Bogside (8.35), East Grange (8.39), Oakley (8.44), Dunfermline (8.56).
20	Larbert (8.38).
35 (Cal.)	Throsk Platform (8.39), Airth (8.48), Larbert (8.55).
47	Dunfermline (Upper) (9.07), (Lower) (9.24), Edinburgh (9.49)
51	Cambus (8.56), Causewayhead (9.04), Stirling (9.07).
9.00	Sauchie (9.05), Tillicoultry (9.10), Dollar (9.16), Rumbling Bridge (9.32), Crook of Devon (9.36), Balado (9.43), Kinross Jct (9.51), Milnathort (9.55), Mawcarse Jct (10.00), Gateside (10.05), Strathmiglo (10.10), Auchtermuchty (10.19), Ladybank (10.30).
21	Larbert (9.37).
25	Cambus (9.30), Causewayhead (9.38), Stirling (9.42), Larbert (9.39), Cowlairs (10.14), Glasgow (10.20).
26	East Grange (9.38), Oakley (9.43), Dunfermline (Upper) (9.54), (Lower) (10.00), Inverkeithing (10.07), North Queensferry (10.14), Dalmeny (10.20), Turnhouse (10.27), Haymarket (10.39), Edinburgh (10.43).
30	Cambus (9.35), Menstrie and Glenochil (9.42), Alva (9.48).
10.05	Cambus (10.11), Causewayhead (10.19), Stirling (10.23), Larbert (10.46), Castlecary (10.58), Dullatur (11.04), Croy (11.10), Lenzie (11.10), Bishopbriggs (11.26), Cowlairs (11.34), Glasgow (11.40).
18	Causewayhead (10.28), Stirling (10.32)
23	Sauchie (10.28), Tillicoultry (10.33), Dollar (10.40), Rumbling Bridge (10.50), Kinross Jct (11.01).
25	Clackmannan and Kennet (10.31), Kilbagie (10.37), Kincardine (10.41).
30	Cambus (10.35), Menstrie and Glenochil (10.39), Alva (10.44).
40	Clackmannan Road (10.45), Forest Mill (10.49), Bogside (10.56), East Grange (11.01), Oakley (11.06), Dunfermline (Upper) (11.25), Halbeath (11.30), Crossgates (11.35), Cowdenbeath (11.41), Kelty (11.46).

PM

12.33 (Cal.)	Throsk Platform (12.37), Airth (12.46), Larbert (12.53).
42	Larbert (1.00), Lenzie (1.25), Bishopbriggs (1.32), Cowlairs (1.41), Glasgow (1.49).
47	Bogside (12.57 Tues. only), East Grange (1.00 Thurs. only), Oakley (1.02 Mon., Wed. and Fri. only), Dunfermline (Upper) (1.11), (Lower) (1.24), Haymarket (1.50), Edinburgh (1.54).

12.50	Cambus (12.56), Causewayhead (1.05), Stirling (1.08).
55	Cambus (1.00), Menstrie and Glenochil (1.07), Alva (1.13).
1.43 (S)	East Grange (1.55), Oakley (2.00), Dunfermline (Upper) (2.11), Cowdenbeath (2.21), Thornton (2.36).
2.19	Causewayhead (2.31), Stirling (2.34).
32	Sauchie (2.37), Tillicoultry (2.42), Dollar (2.48).
40	Larbert (2.59), Castlecary (3.10), Cowlairs (3.33), Glasgow (3.41).
47	Cambus (2.54), Causewayhead (3.04), Stirling (3.12).
50	Tillicoultry (2.58), Dollar (3.05), Rumbling Bridge (3.15), Kinross Jct (3.28), Bridge of Earn (3.49), Perth (3.58).
55	Clackmannan Road (3.00), Forest Mill (3.04), Bogside (3.11), East Grange (3.16), Oakley (3.21), Dunfermline (3.52), Halbeath (3.57), Crossgates (4.02), Cowdenbeath (4.08), Lochgelly (4.15), Cardenden (4.25), Thornton Jct (4.37).
57	Cambus (3.03), Menstrie and Glenochil (3.07), Alva (3.13).
3.00	Clackmannan and Kennet (3.06), Kilbagie (3.12), Kincardine (3.16).
4.05 (Cal.)	Throsk Platform (4.05), Airth (4.18), Larbert (4.25).
18	Oakley (4.34, Sats. only), Dunfermline (Upper) (4.46), (Lower) (5.01), Inverkeithing (5.08), Haymarket (5.34), Edinburgh (5.38).
20	Cambus (4.26), Causewayhead (4.34), Stirling (4.38).
30	Cambus (4.36), Menstrie and Glenochil (4.40), Alva (4.45).
5.21	Causewayhead (5.31), Stirling (5.34).
22	Clackmannan and Kennet (5.28), Kilbagie (5.34), Kincardine (5.38).
22	Sauchie (5.26), Tillicoultry (5.31), Dollar (5.39), Rumbling Bridge (5.49), Crook of Devon (5.53), Balado (5.57), Kinross Jct (6.03).
27	Cambus (5.33), Menstrie and Glenochil (5.37), Alva (5.42).
34	Stirling (5.49), Larbert (6.04), Castlecary (6.18), Dullatur (6.25), Lenzie (6.37), Cowlairs (6.52), Glasgow (7.00).
38	Clackmannan Road (5.43), Forest Mill (5.47), Bogside (5.54), East Grange (5.59), Oakley (6.04), Dunfermline (Upper) (6.15).
45	Tillicoultry (5.53), Dollar (6.00), Rumbling Bridge (6.10), Crook of Devon (6.14), Kinross Jct (6.23), Mawcarse Jct (6.30), Glenfarg (6.38), Bridge of Earn (6.48), Perth (6.55).
6.08	Clackmannan and Kennet (6.14), Kilbagie (6.20), Kincardine (6.24).
13 (Cal.)	Throsk Platform (6.17), Airth (6.25), Larbert (6.32).
18	Cambus (6.23), Causewayhead (6.31), Stirling (6.34).
19	Dunfermline (Upper) (6.45), (Lower) (6.58), Inverkeithing (7.05), N. Queensferry (7.12), Dalmeny (7.18), Turnhouse (7.25), Haymarket (7.35), Edinburgh (7.49).
7.43	Cambus (7.49), Causewayhead (7.58), Stirling (8.01).
8.23	Clackmannan Road (8.28), Forest Mill (8.32), Bogside (8.39), East Grange (8.44), Oakley (8.49), Dunfermline (Upper) (9.03), Halbeath (9.08), Crossgates (9.13), Cowdenbeath (9.19), Lochgelly (9.26), Cardenden (9.35), Thornton (9.47).
26	Tillicoultry (8.34), Dollar (8.41), Rumbling Bridge (8.51), Crook of Devon (8.55), Balado (sets down), Kinross Jct (9.15), Milnathort (9.19), Mawcarse Jct (9.24), Glenfarg (9.33), Bridge of Earn (9.45), Perth (9.52).
40 (S)	Sauchie (8.44), Tillicoultry (8.50).
42 (S)	Clackmannan and Kennet (8.48), Kilbagie (8.54), Kincardine (8.58)
42	Stirling (8.59), Larbert (9.15), Castlecary (9.35), Dullatur (9.42), Croy (9.47), Lenzie (9.56), Cowlairs (10.08), Glasgow (10.14).
45	Cambus (8.51), Causewayhead (8.59), Stirling (9.03).
53	Cambus (9.01), Menstrie and Glenochil (9.08), Alva (9.14).

9.05	Dunfermline (Upper) (9.27), (Lower) (9.35), Inverkeithing (9.43), N. Queensferry (9.46 Sats. only), Dalmeny (9.53), Haymarket (9.07), Edinburgh (10.11).
10.21	Cambus (sets down), Stirling (10.33).

STIRLING & DUNFERMLINE RAILWAY.

SEPTEMBER, 1850.

DOWN TRAINS. From Alloa to Dunfermline, &c.

Miles.	STATIONS.	1 — 1, 2, 4, Class. Parly.	2 — 1, 2, 3, Class.	3 — Classes 1, 2, 3,	4 — Classes 1, 2, 3,	1st Class. s. D.	2nd Class. s. D.	3rd Class. s. D.	4th Class. s. D.
	Trains leave Dunfermline by Edinburgh, Perth, & Dundee Railway, for	A.M.	A.M.	P.M.	P.M.				
	EDINBURGH, PERTH, DUNDEE at	7 0	10 25	3 25	7 30				
	And Arrive at		P.M.			**Through Fares from Alloa.**			
	EDINBURGH........about	9 25	12 40	5 45	9 45	3 6	3 0	2 3	2 0
	PERTH................about	9 20	12 30	5 35	9 45	11 5	9 7	7 0	4 8
	DUNDEE.............about	10 0	1 10	6 20	10 5	11 11	9 10	7 3	4 11
	For arrival and departure of Trains at Intermediate Stations on Edinburgh, Perth, and Dundee Railway, see their Time Bills.					**Fares on Stirling and Dunfermline Railway.**			
	Trains leave	A.M.	A.M.	P.M.	P.M.				
	ALLOA,....................	6 15	9 40	2 40	6 45				
2¾	CLACKMANNAN,..........	6 23	9 48	2 48	6 53	0 5	0 4	0 3	0 2
3½	KINCARDINE,.............	6 27	9 52	2 52	6 27	0 9	0 7	0 6	0 4
9½	OAKLEY,..................	6 45	10 10	3 10	7 15	1 11	1 6	1 2	0 9
14½	*Arrive at* DUNFERMLINE,.........	7 0	10 25	3 25	7 30	2 11	2 4	1 9	1 2

UP TRAINS. From Dunfermline to Alloa, &c.

Miles.	STATIONS.	1 — Classes 1, 2, 4, Parly.	2 — Classes 1, 2, 3,	3 — Classes 1, 2, 3,	4 — Classes 1, 2, 3,	1st Class. s. D.	2d Class. s. D.	3d Class. s. D.	4th Class. s. D.
	Trains leave the following Places by the Edinburgh, Perth, and Dundee Railway.	A.M.	A.M.	P.M.	P.M.				
	EDINBURGH,.............at	6 30	9 45	3 0	7 0				
	PERTH,....................at	6 30	9 45	3 0	7 0	For through Fares to Alloa see Table of Rates on List of Down Trains.			
	DUNDEE,..................at	5 50	9 5	2 20	6 20				
	And Arrive at DUNFERMLINE,......about	8 50	12 0	5 7	9 13				
	For arrival and departure of Trains at Intermediate Stations on Edinr., Perth, and Dundee Railway, see their Time Bills.					**Fares on Stirling and Dunfermline Railway.**			
	Trains Leave	A.M.	A.M.	P.M.	P.M.				
	DUNFERMLINE,...........	8 50	12 0	5 7	9 13				
4¾	OAKLEY,..................	9 5	12 15	5 22	9 28	1 1	0 10	0 8	0 5
10½	KINCARDINE,.............	9 23	12 33	5 40	9 46	2 3	1 9	1 4	0 11
11¾	CLACKMANNAN,..........	9 27	12 37	5 44	9 50	2 6	2 0	1 6	1 0
14	*Arrive at* ALLOA,....	9 30	12 45	5 52	9 58	2 11	2 4	1 9	1 2

RETURN TICKETS are issued daily between Alloa and Dunfermline at the following Rates:—First Class 4s. 6d.; Second Class 3s. 6d.; Third Class 2s. 8d.; and between Alloa and Edinburgh, Leith. or Granton at 5s. 3d. First Class; 4s. 6d. Second Class; 3s. 4d. Third Class; and 3s. Fourth Class. Return Tickets are only available for the Station for which they are granted, and if presented at any other Station the full fare will be charged.

See Time Bills for Regulations and Conditions.

By Order of the Directors,
JAMES MONTEATH, Secretary.

Edinburgh, 2d September 1850.

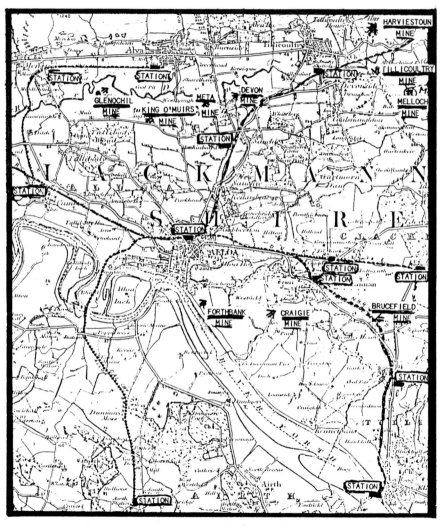

Clackmannanshire – 18th and 19th centuries rail and coal developments –
Rail lines, stations and mines

BOOK REVIEW

AGRICULTURAL IMPROVEMENT IN STRATHKELVIN 1700-1850.
Dorothy E. McGuire. Strathkelvin, Auld Kirk Museum Publications
No. 15. 128pp. 1988. ISBN 0 904966 20 8. £4.50.

Strathkelvin District Libraries and Museums have established an
excellent record in publishing, a reputation to which Dorothy McGuire's
volume makes a further contribution.

Improvement, the process by which changes in agricultural practice
transformed Scotland's rural landscape, is a path well-trodden by
historians. It had its own contemporary literature, in Wight's *Surveys*,
in the *General Views of Agriculture* and in the *Statistical Accounts*; the
availability of these contemporary accounts has led historians rather too
often, to swallow whole their opinions and prejudices as if their's was
the whole truth and nothing but the truth. Worse still, the now standard
works by Haldane and Symon can become quarries from which material
is extracted directly, without any awareness of inherent bias.

To her credit, Dorothy McGuire has avoided this pitfall. While making
exhaustive use of published material she has supplemented this with
unpublished primary sources, notably the Stirling of Keir and Cadder
Papers and the Lennox of Woodhead Papers. Furthermore, she makes
good use of work by second generation writers such as Whyte and
Dodgshon, who have helped to refine our perceptions of pre-
Improvement conditions.

A short introduction sets the scene, followed by a systematic series
of thematic chapters. Chapter one, on environment, notes the interest
of Improvement writers in climate, relief and soil conditions but, rather
than regurgitating their writings, uses the work of modern soil scientists
to describe conditions. Chapter two introduces the human dimension
in the form of tenure. Inevitably the complexities of landholding have
been simplified, so that attention focusses on tenants of estates, whose
affairs are, in any case better documented than those of feuars or 'bonnet'
lairds. I was left wondering whether either of these latter groups were
to be found at all in Strathkelvin.

The next three chapters, on enclosure, drainage and wasteland
demonstrate how the Improvers' ideas were put into effect to modify
the agricultural landscape. McGuire recognises the key importance of
tile drainage and the drainage Acts of the 1840s, points which are
sometimes overlooked, but makes no reference to mechanisation in drain
tile and drain pipe manufacture, from the late 1830s, without which the
'drainage revolution' could not have been carried through so rapidly.
The chapters on enclosure and the improvement of wasteland might have
been an opportunity to illustrate inter-relations within both pre- and post-
Improvement farming: not until the advent of enclosed *parks* for sown

grasses could wasteland be dispensed with. Land producing only cereals and pulses could have remained open indefinitely, but only by sowing grass crops, within enclosures, could a break be made in the pre-Improvement cycle of interdependence under which wasteland had to stay out of cultivation in order to feed livestock.

Chapters seven, eight and nine investigate the annual cycle of cultivation, the crops grown and the livestock kept. A chapter on rural life concentrates on the agricultural labour force, but also describes the diet and fuel supply of the whole farming community. Day labourers, an often neglected group, are given their rightful prominence, as is their decline as new technologies and specialised trades developed.

The interdependence between agriculture and its increasingly urbanised and industrialised markets provides the subject matter for the book's last three chapters. This is an essential part of the story, as McGuire recognises, for the existene of alternative employment opportunities, off the land, were an important force in pushing Improvement through.

Appendices, a glossary, bibliography and index round off a very thorough, scholarly work, well annotated with notes and references and illustrated within the text and in separate plates. The preface notes that its original purpose was to have been a reference book for secondary pupils but seems to concede it is perhaps too advanced to serve this need. However, the author has succeeded in producing a work which is essential reading for anyone with a local or specialist interest.

John Shaw, 1989

Editorial Note — Beetles

A year or two ago the Secretary of the AEC (Asociación europea coleopteralogia) at Barcelona University asked to exchange publications with us, and we have their bulletin volumes 1 and 2 — *Elytron*, 1987 and 1988, of some 120 and 160 pages respectively. I believe it is available elsewhere including Glasgow and Edinburgh universities, and the Glasgow Natural History Society, but I will happily copy the contents or lend to anyone interested.

STIRLING DISTRICT LIBRARIES COMMUNITY HERITAGE PROJECT

Andrew Muirhead

From August 1985 to November 1987, Stirling District Libraries acted as hosts to a Manpower Services funded scheme set up to index the *Stirling Observer* from its foundation in 1836. The decision was taken to index all local references including advertisements and announcements. A team of indexers, largely unemployed graduates and clerical assistants, was recruited and work started. For the sake of continuity, indexers had their own volumes to work through, and it was interesting to notice they became involved in stories as they developed from week to week. In addition to the indexing, the staff were given the opportunity to research local history topics, more or less of their own choice, and six booklets appropriately illustrated were the result. Sadly, it was not possible to continue the project longer than two and a quarter years, but the result is that the Central Region Archive now holds a very detailed index of the first 30 years of the *Stirling Observer* in card index form. Also files relating to individual people, were transferred to a micro-computer and produced as the book *People 1836-56*. These files include not only general references to local people, but also births, deaths and marriage announcements, and victims of crimes.

Four of the six booklets and the printed index are available from Stirling District Libraries; the booklets at 75p each and the index at £3.50, plus postage if by mail.

Also available from FN&H or SDL are two fine collections of historial local photographs – *Bridge of Allan . . .* 64pp £3.25 and *Drymen . . .* 48pp £2.50 (50p p&p on these).

Editorial Note — Man IN the Landscape

These occasional events are related to or complement the Man AND the Landscape symposia — Inchcailloch in 1980, sailing the windings of the Forth in 1981, the Ochils weather station Carim in 1982, and last summer two voyages on the Forth. The first in July was a small hospitality party aboard the Gardiloo captained by Ronald Reask — a very enjoyable allday Leith to Bell Rock voyage to dump Lothian Region sewage. BBC reporter John Knox was with us and I have a recording of his broadcast (c20 minutes) — particularly relevant now since this March's European conference and agreements on North Sea pollution. The second was a chartered evening cruise aboard the Maid of the Forth from Queensferry to Kincardine Power Station, with commentaries by Donald McLusky and Mike Elliott, providing for the 130 aboard a useful introduction to the Estuary — theme of the November symposium.

This year we hope to have a similar cruise on Loch Lomond to complement the symposium — see p114.